Summon
up the Blood

Summon up the Blood

In dogged pursuit of the blood cell regulators

D ONALD M ETCALF

[handwritten signature]

α AlphaMed Press

α AlphaMed Press, One Prestige Place, Suite 290, Miamisburg, Ohio 45342-3758 USA.

Cover design by Bil Myers
Text set in Times Roman by Robert Wexler
Manufactured in the United States of America

Library of Congress Cataloging-in-Publication Data
Metcalf, Donald
Summon up the Blood: In dogged pursuit of the blood cell growth regulators
by Donald Metcalf.

p. cm.

Includes bibliographic references and index.
Library of Congress Control Number: 1-88085-427-9 (hard cover)
Library of Congress Control Number: 1-88085-428-7 (soft cover)

        1. Blood   2. Medicine—history
        I. Title   II. Metcalf, Donald

573.15 dc   CIP 00-131685

To the 329 able scientists and clinicians who worked together in our studies on the colony-stimulating factors and to our colleagues and competitors in the field.

Professor Donald Metcalf

AC, MD BSc (Med) FRCPA FRACP Hon DSc Syd,
Hon MD Oslo, FAA FRS
Professor Emeritus, The Walter and Eliza Hall Institute of
Medical Research
Melbourne, Australia

Professor Donald Metcalf

A Profile

Professor Donald Metcalf was born in Mittagong, New South Wales, Australia, and was educated in various country schools. He graduated from Sydney University in 1953 after completing a BSc (Med) in virology. After an internship at The Royal Prince Alfred Hospital, Sydney, he joined the staff of The Walter and Eliza Hall Institute of Medical Research in Melbourne in 1954 as the Carden Fellow in Cancer Research, a position he continues to hold. From 1965 to 1996, he was Head of the Cancer Research Unit and Assistant Director of The Walter and Eliza Hall Institute, and in 1996 became Professor Emeritus of The University of Melbourne.

His work at The Walter and Eliza Hall Institute has been interspersed with sabbatical years as a Visiting Scientist at Harvard Medical School, Boston; the Roswell Park Memorial Institute, Buffalo; the Swiss Institute for Experimental Cancer Research, Lausanne; the Radiobiological Institute, Rijswijk, and the University of Cambridge.

Professor Metcalf has been rightfully called "the father of hematopoietic cytokines" for his pioneering work on the control of blood cell formation. In early studies, he discovered the function of the thymus gland in controlling the formation of lymphocytes, and beginning in 1965, co-developed a series of specialized culture techniques permitting the growth of the various types of blood cells. These cultures led him and his team to the discovery of the "colony-stimulating factors" (CSFs), hormones that control white blood cell formation and are, therefore, responsible for one's resistance to infection. His work, with that of others, led to the successful cloning of the genes for all four mouse and human CSFs, and the mass production of these hormones by bacterial, yeast, and other cells. His work provided the pivotal demonstration that the CSFs, when injected into animals, stimulated the formation and regulated the activity of white blood cells. Exploiting this, his collaborators then documented the effectiveness of GM-CSF and G-CSF (two primary white blood cell regulators) when injected into patients. These blood cell regulators are now in extensive clinical use throughout the world as valuable drugs, which can accelerate the regrowth of blood cells following anti-cancer treatment and bone marrow or peripheral blood transplantation.

The corpus of his fundamental and applied research is to be found in more than 400 peer-reviewed scientific papers, 200 other scientific papers, and seven books. Professor Metcalf has received some of the highest honors in the world of contemporary science. Among them, he was made a Companion of the Order of Australia; he was elected a Fellow of the Australian Academy of Science, a Fellow of the Royal Society, London; and a Foreign Associate of the National Academy of Sciences of the U.S. His prizes for research include the Wellcome Prize of the Royal Society (shared), the Bristol-Myers Award for Distinguished Achievement in Cancer Research, the Hammer Prize for Cancer, the Koch Prize of the Federal Republic of Germany, and a Gairdner Foundation International Award of Canada. In addition, Professor Metcalf shared the Alfred P. Sloan Prize of the General Motors Cancer Research Foundation; received the Bertner Foundation Award of the MD Anderson Cancer Center, and the Rabbi Shai Shacknai Prize of the Hadassah University, Jerusalem. He is also a recipient of the Albert Lasker Clinical Medical Research Award, the Louisa Gross Horwitz Prize of Columbia University, the Jessie Stevenson Kovalenko Medal of the U.S. National Academy of Sciences, and was the inaugural recipient of the Kantor Family Prize for Cancer Research Excellence from the Hipple Cancer Research Center. In 1995 he received the Ernst Neumann Award, International Society for Experimental Hematology and the Royal Medal, Royal Society, London. In 1996 he shared the Amgen Australia Prize and The Warren Alpert Foundation Prize, Harvard Medical School. In 1998 he was made an Honorary Member of the Alpha Omega Alpha Medical Society, U.S. and in 2000 he will receive the Chiron International Award, National Academy of Medicine, Italy.

Unusual among scientists of almost any age, certainly those in their seventh decade of life, he continues to work at the laboratory bench nine hours each day. The brilliant and incredibly productive life of Professor Metcalf may be viewed in this book as a magnificent painting, but one of its primary colors would be missing without recognition of the loving support of Josephine, his wife of 46 years. Mother of their four grown daughters, "Jo" (as she is affectionately called) has been a tower of strength and a source of perspective for Don, their children and grandchildren, and for all those fortunate to know and thereby to be touched by her. Therein lies another profile...and another fascinating book.

Once more unto the breach, dear friends, once more;
Or close the wall up with our English dead!
In peace there's nothing so becomes a man
As modest stillness and humility;
But when the blast of war blows in our ears,
Then imitate the action of the tiger:
Stiffen the sinews, summon up the blood,
Disguise fair nature with hard-favour'd rage;
Then lend the eye a terrible aspect.

William Shakespeare
King Henry V
Act III, Scene 1

The first two lines of this excerpt were used by me on more than one occasion as an exhortation to my colleagues when things were going badly and spirits were sagging. Not that we were English, but we were being sorely tried.

Donald Metcalf

Acknowledgments

I am, as always, indebted to Elizabeth Hodgson who faithfully typed this manuscript and every one of our manuscripts on the colony-stimulating factors from 1965. I am also indebted to various of our Institute's photographers for their staff and technical photographs. Finally, I am indebted to Dr. Ann Murphy for her careful editorial review of the manuscript and for allowing most of my Australian English to survive transcription into American English.

Contents

Introduction   1

1   The Beginnings   5

2   Project Goals and Approaches   21

3   Was the Colony-Stimulating Factor Likely
      to be a Regulator?   27

4   The Purification of CSF from Human Urine   33

5   The Dubious Joys of Bioassays   47

6   The Discovery and Purification of GM-CSF   59

7   The Discovery and Purification of G-CSF   71

8   The Discovery and Purification of
      Multi-CSF (IL-3)   83

9   The End of the Beginning: An Appraisal
      of Progress So Far   93

10   The Cloning of the CSF Genes   107

11   The Recombinant CSFs In Vitro and
        at Last In Vivo   123

12   The Clinical Use of the CSFs   139

13   The Cloning and Characterization of Receptors
        for the CSFs and Other Regulators   153

14   The Role of the CSFs in Myeloid Leukemia   167

15   In Vivo Manipulation of CSF Genes   187

16   The Bottom Lines   197

     Appendix   203

     Suggested Further Readings   209

     Index   211

Cover legend:
The cover photograph captures the essence of the story—teamwork, with the two main players in the discovery of G-CSF, Don Metcalf (right) and Nick Nicola. Ray Bradley's astonishing bone marrow colonies are highlighted on the cover's margin and spine (photographs are reproduced with permission from the Archives of The Walter and Eliza Hall Institute of Medical Research).

Introduction

The 35-year saga of the discovery, development, and medical application of the blood cell regulators, the colony-stimulating factors (CSFs), has all the elements needed for an absorbing story. There was a cast of characters who shared between them a full range of human foibles, the gradual opening of an exciting new field of medical science, distrust between opposing groups, the tedium of endless purifications, the excitement of gene cloning and expression, the tensions of animal then clinical trials, opportunities lost, battles over patent rights, the aggression or indolence of pharmaceutical companies, the frustrations of licensing procedures, and always the need to push techniques and ideas beyond existing limits.

Despite repeated requests, I had been reluctant to attempt to write a semipopular account of the CSFs, suspecting correctly that this might prove to be quite difficult. However, those of us who were involved from the early phases have been chagrined to realize that we have already begun to forget key elements of the story. There seemed no other option therefore than to set down as many of the details as could be recalled before too much else was forgotten.

As most of the participants in the saga are still alive and remain on friendly, if sometimes wary, terms, I certainly had no inclination to write a warts-and-all exposé. I do have my own views on certain episodes where tensions arose but I am not well placed to describe how others felt or acted at these times.

This book was not intended to be an ordered and fully referenced scientific account of the CSFs. Such an account has already been written by Nick Nicola and me. Rather, I wished to give a chronological description of how order slowly emerged out of confusion in this field, and to attempt this without becoming so technical that a nonexpert reader would become discouraged.

My attempt to write a blow-by-blow account soon ran into difficulties. It was easy enough to write a personal account of the early days of the project when only three or four workers were involved. This became much more difficult when there were a hundred or so in various groups working in the field. It clearly became impossible to introduce any personal touches to the account when there probably were thousands involved in various aspects of the work.

By default, the account became progressively transformed to a skewed description of the activities of a single research group. This then became in danger of implying that we were the only serious contributors to the field. I have tried to avoid this distortion by inserting at various stages the important contributions of others but may not have been wholly successful in this attempt.

It became increasingly more difficult to describe, in the form of a single account, a story that became composed of quite separate issues and projects, proceeding simultaneously. In the latter part of the book, this problem forced a divergence from a single chronological account to separate descriptions of four major streams of work that were really proceeding simultaneously.

Try as I could, the account could not be restricted to the CSFs. Other hematopoietic regulators were being discovered as the work on the CSFs progressed and, because these often interact with the CSFs, they needed to be introduced from time to time.

No account of the development of the CSFs was able to be given without some reference to the target hematopoietic cells on which they act, because the characterization of these cells was making major advances throughout the period of work on the CSFs. So, from time to time, there were necessary asides in the account to fill the reader in on these simultaneous developments.

Work on the CSFs did not cease with their clinical development. Much further crucial information on these regulators needed to be discovered and indeed these studies continue today. The latter part of the account therefore is a description of what we and others felt impelled to do in the postclinical era.

While most of the salient features of the CSF story have at least been mentioned, the account has ended up neither fish nor fowl. It is heavily autobiographical but without many of the expected features of an autobiography. I have tried to portray laboratory life as it happens for a group tackling complex and prolonged projects and I hope this gives some insights into how findings slowly emerge. The description omits dramas, personal frictions, and periods of angst that of course occurred and possibly can be read between the lines.

What has resulted may well be a rather dull account of a subject that could have made a sustaining page-turner. It is interesting, in the development and expansion of a subject, how the intensely personal excitements for the few in the initial days do transform to a somewhat shapeless pattern as the field expands: advances go on, but in a manner that progressively appears to lose its personal aspects. For each individual this may never actually be the case, but as more and more investigators enter a field it becomes almost impossible to follow in detail their individual hopes and actions.

I have ended up with an account that is little more than a history of a single research unit over the past 35 years. This may interest those who know the field and perhaps not many others. If this is the case, so be it. If my account does not seem to agree with accounts of the CSFs that often appear in more recent review publications, then I suggest that the readers go back to the scientific literature and establish exactly who did what and when. They may find some surprises.

Donald Metcalf
Melbourne, 2000

ONE

The Beginnings

B y tradition, stories are best begun with the phrase "It was a dark and stormy night....," but I cannot now remember whether the colony-stimulating factor (CSF) story began for me in the morning or afternoon. It was certainly not night, and I doubt strongly whether it could have been raining.

For my temerity in wishing to do cancer research in an immunological institute, The Walter and Eliza Hall Institute of Medical Research in Melbourne, Australia, I had been exiled from the main Institute building in 1958 to some small laboratories in the Institute's animal house. This was a noisome building in an adjacent veterinary precinct, accessible from the Institute by a long tunnel under the Royal Melbourne Hospital, which then passed through the laundry block and around the hospital rubbish dump. For someone highly allergic to all animals, particularly mice, it was an unfortunate location in which to spend eight years, but despite this, our little group was happy and productive, if somewhat isolated and disregarded.

We were funded entirely by the Anti-Cancer Council of Victoria and our self-chosen scientific brief was to attempt to understand the nature of the leukemias and the mechanisms involved in the development of these diseases. This had considerable bearing on the curious manner in which we were to undertake some of our work on the CSFs. The particular approach we adopted was to explore the possibility that, like tumors of endocrine target tissues, the leukemias might arise at least in part as a consequence of an imbalance in the regulatory factors controlling blood cell proliferation. This notion was to prove to have some validity, but the approach had an obvious initial requirement—to establish the existence and nature of these unknown regulatory factors that were being postulated as controlling blood cell formation.

When these studies began in the mid-1950s only one regulator of hematopoiesis had been identified with any sort of experimental validation. This was erythropoietin, an agent believed to regulate red cell formation. Even for erythropoietin, the evidence supporting its reality and possible mode of action was minimal by today's standards.

One of the most promising alternative leads in the early 1950s was that the thymus seemed to be essential for the development of lymphoid leukemia in mice. The thymus might not only be producing lymphocytes but might also act as a regulator of lymphocytes throughout the body. Some of my early work, which others were never able to repeat, suggested that thymus extracts, when injected into baby mice, could elevate blood lymphocyte levels. This work led me into a decade of exploring the consequences of thymectomy and an analysis of how cell production in the thymus appeared to be regulated. This latter question remains to be properly resolved, and in the early 1960s, with the necessity of using whole animal models, it was certainly not feasible to dig very deeply into the possible operating mechanisms. My small group persisted, but we were very conscious of the fact that whole animal work had severe limitations and that we were confronted by a technically impassable barrier. We were eager for some simpler system that would allow hematopoietic regulators to be characterized and were ready with a long list of questions for resolution using such a system. Indeed, we were in a thoroughly primed but frustrated state.

A visit in 1964 by a colleague was to make a dramatic impact on the direction of our future activities. Ray Bradley, who was working across the street from the Institute at the University of Melbourne, came to our laboratories one day with a small metal tray. He and I had collaborated in former years on a number of studies exploring the repopulation of thymus and spleen grafts, but what he was carrying was something radically different. He had brought along for my enlightenment and com-

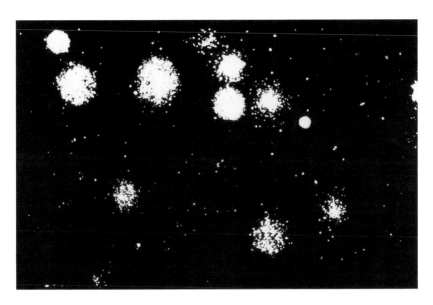

Ray Bradley's astonishing bone marrow colonies.

ments a set of carefully handled glass petri dishes containing semisolid agar cultures of mouse bone marrow cells in which extraordinary colonies had developed.

I challenge anyone on first seeing such colonies not to be astonished and intrigued. These colonies are three-dimensional populations of cells of wonderfully variable shapes and sizes, and look like galaxies as approached by a fast-moving spaceship. Their beauty continues to fascinate me, even after 35 years.

Bone Marrow Cultures: A Background

The context in which the arrival of these colonies occurred underscored their dramatic impact. Prior to the 1960s, many workers had attempted to culture bone marrow cell populations in conventional liquid suspension cultures. The results were indifferent and such cultures appeared unable to achieve dramatic increases in cell numbers. The populations being cultured were a confusing mixture of different hematopoietic cells at differing stages of maturation. Although some cell division could be seen to be occurring, simultaneous cell death and maturation made it impossible to interpret what was happening and no consistent patterns emerged.

In retrospect, it is a little difficult to imagine why more satisfactory results had not been obtained because bone marrow cells have a robust capacity to proliferate, even under fairly adverse circumstances, and experience with the culture of cells like fibroblasts was reasonably extensive by the mid-1960s.

However, the mid-1960s did mark the beginning of an abrupt improvement in tissue culture technology. The precise composition of culture medium that was adequate for mammalian cells had been defined by Eagle and Earle, among others. While such media initially still had to be prepared by hand in individual laboratories, this was about to change with the introduction of commercially available pow-dered media formulated simply to require the addition of water. Plastic culture dishes and flasks of nontoxic materials were about to become commercially available, as were incubators designed to deliver a CO_2–air mixture satisfactory for supporting the survival and growth of mammalian cells. For an institute such as ours that had never under-taken tissue culture, these developments were to have a major impact on our ability to enter this field and achieve some consistency in results obtained. Even in the mid-1960s, however, all cultures were still per-formed in optically imperfect glass petri dishes or flasks, requiring careful rewashing before re-use. What was later to become a trivial matter of preparing 100 petri dish cultures, at that time, still represented a major logistical exercise.

It also became very apparent in this period that the standard serum additive required for such cultures, fetal calf serum (FCS), was a far from predictable entity. With inferior FCS, no cell growth occurred, but with other apparently similar batches, good growth was obtainable. To this day, what makes serum batches good or bad remains largely unknown, but it gradually became apparent that pretesting of batches was essential before purchase of a batch for use. Such tests had to be carried out on the actual cell populations destined for study because results from the culture of one cell type did not reliably certify the ade-quacy of the serum for other types of culture. These screening tests are still necessary, but at least now companies are aware of these technical problems and are ready to supply samples of FCS batches for such pretesting.

Before these improvements occurred, tissue culture in the mid-1960s had many of the elements of home cooking, the consequent variability often causing confusion regarding the results obtained and obscuring phenomena that should have otherwise been observable.

The use of media made semisolid by inclusion of agar was to prove a vital step in allowing order to emerge from confusion, because the progeny of dividing cells remained physically adjacent, resulting in the development of visually obvious colonies. Usually the other cells in the original cultured population died during the incubation period of one to two weeks, leaving the areas between developing colonies relatively cell-free and emphasizing the dramatic visual impact of the proliferating colonies of cells. Agar cultures had been introduced into experimental research to define a difference in growth behavior between untransformed fibroblasts (unable to grow in agar culture) and transformed or sarcomatous fibroblasts (which could proliferate and form colonies). This was a useful and reliable maneuver for those working on viral transformation of fibroblasts. Why the difference should have been so reproducible remains a mystery because normal fibroblasts, or at least their precursors, can, in fact, proliferate well in agar cultures—no doubt under somewhat different culture conditions from those used originally.

In another series of studies, Theodore Puck in Denver had recently shown that single cells could be successfully cultured if the cultures also contained tissues, cells, or medium from cultures of such cells, usually in a separate agar underlayer. The concept proposed was that these various maneuvers prevented loss of important metabolites from the cultured cell by providing a reverse gradient of such metabolites. This interpretation may have some validity, particularly if the culture medium is suboptimal, but nowadays we would interpret the phenomenon as indicating the necessity for a specific growth factor to be produced by, or be present in, the added conditioning cells or medium. This general approach of coculture of cells of interest with underlayers of other cells or tissues was to prove crucial for the successful growth of the first bone marrow-derived colonies.

The final technical advance occurring in the mid-1960s that was of great importance in allowing the rapid screening of cultured bone marrow colonies was the development by the Olympus Company in Tokyo of a simple stereo zoom dissection microscope. This microscope permitted hours of continuous use with little optical strain and was superbly suited for the analysis of bone marrow cultures. Oddly enough, subsequent modifications of this instrument are markedly inferior to the model developed in the mid-1960s, and the original model has become a jealously guarded instrument by those fortunate enough to possess one.

In retrospect, it is therefore now possible to recognize that the mid-1960s was a time of abrupt advances in what was achievable using tissue cultures. It was almost inevitable that somebody during this period was going to stumble across the phenomenon of colony formation by hematopoietic cells. The fact that two groups did so, and quite independently, was not only not surprising—it was almost predictable. The phenomenon of simultaneous discovery has now become commonplace in experimental biology and often has similar general origins, namely the occurrence of advances in technology that now make certain types of experiments feasible or results interpretable.

There was also a certain inevitability about how Ray Bradley came to hit upon the culture technique. He had just spent time as a visiting scientist in Michael Potter's group at the National Institutes of Health (NIH) and had been approached by him repeatedly to try to grow Michael's favorite tumor cells, mouse plasmacytoma cells, in vitro. He had also spent time in the Imperial Cancer Research Fund (ICRF) laboratories in London, where he had become familiar with their use of semisolid agar culture as a selective culture system for transformed versus normal fibroblasts. It seemed to him that agar cultures might permit the growth of neoplastic lymphocytes and, on his return to Melbourne, he approached me for supplies of mouse lymphoma cells.

I had a colony of AKR mice that spontaneously develop thymic lymphomas, and these were the cells he attempted to grow in agar cultures. Nothing grew, but, bearing in mind Puck's experiments, he explored the possible value of including various tissues or cell suspensions as feeder cells in an agar underlayer. One of the cell suspensions used was bone marrow cells and, to his delight, colonies did develop in the cultures. However, closer inspection revealed that the colonies were actually in the underlayers of bone marrow cells, not in the layer contain-

Ray Bradley in later years.

ing the lymphoma cells. Never one to be put down for long by the vagaries of fate, Ray accepted what was being offered—a method for growing colonies of bone marrow cells. He therefore reversed the cultures and used agar underlayers of lymphoma cells to stimulate bone marrow colony formation.

While this system worked well enough, other tissues seemed more active and for some time Ray favored the use of trypsinized kidney cells as his preferred method for stimulating colony formation by bone marrow cells.

It was midway through these experiments that Ray Bradley approached me with his colonies, both to let me know what had been done with my AKR lymphoma cells and to seek assistance with some puzzling aspects of the colony cells. I suspect he did not realize what a startling impact the sight of these colonies was going to have on me or my subsequent work. These colonies were a quantum jump from the previous gloom associated with attempts to culture bone marrow cells and offered me, in my search for hematopoietic regulators, a possible escape from my decade of frustration in attempting to work with the complexity of whole-animal models.

Early Work with Bone Marrow Colonies

The specific reason why Ray Bradley approached me with his colonies was his uncertainty regarding the nature of the cells proliferating in the colonies. As someone whose experience with mouse hematopoietic cells was fairly diverse, it was apparent to me that some colonies were composed of granulocytic cells at varying stages of maturation. Other colonies appeared to be composed of mononuclear cells that could have been macrophages but contained metachromatic granules, which gave them the appearance in Giemsa-stained preparations of being mast cells. Other colonies contained cells of both types.

Were the mononuclear cells really mast cells? We were fairly skeptical and tested them for their ability to phagocytose carbon particles. They were clearly active phagocytically so we considered them, despite their appearance, probably to be macrophages. It is interesting to read in our initial publications how we, to some degree, skirted the issue by calling these cells "mononuclear cells"—that is, cells usually having a round nucleus. At that time it was not uncommon to refer to macrophages as mononuclear cells or phagocytic mononuclear cells but the term mononuclear cells has since been dropped from general usage for these cells. We presumed that, by phagocytosing agar from the surrounding medium, which is itself metachromatic, these cells had acquired the appearance of mast cells. This seemed a slightly improbable hypothesis, given the regularity of size of the granules, but nonetheless was proved to be correct by Israeli colleagues who eventually solved the problem by using methylcellulose as an alternative agent to form the semisolid medium. In such cultures, the mononuclear cells were now free of metachromatic granules and were much more obviously macrophage in nature.

From his initial experiments, Ray Bradley had established some very important aspects concerning colony formation by bone marrow cells. The number of colonies developing was linear with respect to cultured cell numbers, suggesting strongly, but not proving, that each colony was in fact a clone formed by a single initiating cell. If so, many granulocytes and macrophages must share a common ancestral colony-forming cell, and these two morphologically very different cell lineages must in fact be very closely related.

More important from my point of view, Ray had documented that colony formation was not spontaneous. No colonies formed unless underlayer feeder cells were incorporated in the cultures. This opened up a number of radically different possibilities: (1) that, as suggested by Puck, the underlayer tissues were preventing loss of intracellular components from the cultured cells, permitting their survival and allowing them to exhibit an intrinsic capacity for unstimulated proliferation; (2) that something specific was being produced by the underlayer cells, which possibly represented a regulatory factor for cell division by granulocytes and macrophages; or (3) that what was being observed was in vitro transformation of marrow cells, possibly by some virus being released from the cocultured cells, with the agar cultures then allowing the selective growth of the transformed cells.

These conflicting possibilities were to remain as recurring nightmares for some years as work on bone marrow colonies progressed. Naturally, with my background of thymic growth factors and hopes to uncover hematopoietic growth factors, I preferred the second possibility, but the folklore surrounding the selective growth in agar of transformed fibroblasts could not be disregarded, even though the marrow-derived colony cells appeared to be exhibiting normal enough maturation. The first possibility, that the phenomenon was trivial in nature, was too horrible to contemplate but was never able to be properly eliminated until biochemical analysis began to indicate the special macromolecular nature of the active material coming from the cocultured cells.

Despite all these uncertainties, we felt that a descriptive paper on this astonishing phenomenon was appropriate even though we could offer no convincing interpretation upon which to base the phenomenon.

Preparation of manuscripts was not then the matter of urgency it has now become, although the manuscript was submitted for publication in 1965. The journal chosen was less than ideal. It was a local Australian journal, because at this time we were passing through a somewhat dubious nationalistic phase in which we were being encouraged to publish in local scientific journals. This practice proved to be a disaster from the point of view of effectively disseminating information to international colleagues with little access to, or interest in, Australian journals. More importantly, the journal chosen did not record submission dates of manuscripts, merely acceptance dates, and our manuscript, in fact, had a long publication delay. For this reason, our paper on bone marrow colony formation did not appear until 1966, with some unfortunate long-term consequences.

Friction That Should Never Have Arisen

Unknown to us, similar culture work had been in progress simultaneously in the Weizmann Institute, Rehovot, Israel, in the laboratory of Leo Sachs and his Ph.D. student, Dov Pluznik. Agar cultures of murine spleen cells were being used with underlayers of embryo or kidney cells. Again, colony formation was being observed—I presume the same mixture of startled interest and puzzlement. The colonies were originally described as being composed of mast cells, because the cells again showed metachromatic granules characteristic of this cell type. Again, linearity of colony formation with cultured cell numbers was documented as was the necessity to use cocultured underlayer cells, but, importantly, it was found that these could be replaced by the addition of conditioned medium from such cells. These observations were published in *Journal of Cellular and Comparative Physiology* (December 1965) and *Experimental Cell Research* (1966) in the form of two papers describing mast cell colony formation.

How do I know that the Melbourne and Rehovot observations were being made independently and simultaneously? It happened that Leo Sachs and I were both present at an NCI-sponsored meeting on murine leukemia held at the Sheraton Hotel in Philadelphia in October 1965. Following the after-dinner speech by Ludwig Gross, we fell into conversation and Sachs described to me their new culture system giving "funny little" mast cell colonies. It all sounded familiar to me, and I then told him how we also were growing hematopoietic colonies in agar, but that these were composed of granulocytes and probably macrophages. I do not know what happened exactly following Sachs' return to the Weizmann Institute. Suffice it to say that a paper by Ichikawa, Pluznik, and Sachs, describing granulocyte-macrophage colony formation later appeared in the *Proceedings of the National*

Academy of Science with a submission date of May 1966. Reprints of their two earlier papers have quotation marks around the word *mast* (i.e., "mast" cells) in the title and text, in one case in print and the other added by hand in pen.

Why do I bother to describe these events in detail knowing that simultaneous discoveries are commonplace? The point is that the discoveries of Bradley and Pluznik really were an important technical breakthrough that were to have far-reaching consequences in experimental hematology. They marked the beginning of a new era of cellular hematopoiesis, allowing major advances in our understanding of the complex cellular events occurring during hematopoiesis. Primacy of discoveries of this type has every right to be acknowledged and honored, because such quantum leaps are rare. What we always felt to be offensive was the repeated claim, both spoken and in print, that we in Melbourne had merely copied the Rehovot technique and had done so without acknowledgment of their alleged prior work. We felt this was close to a charge of intellectual theft, a serious matter indeed, but one we could not refute because of the failure of the Australian journal to publish submission dates. This repeated abrasive claim was to lead to sustained antagonism in Melbourne that remains to the present day, the more so, when it was reinforced by subsequent disputation regarding the nature, biochemistry, and actions of the CSFs.

What could have been a subsequent two decades of happy characterization of the active factors regulating hematopoiesis, with perhaps useful exchanges of reagents or collaborative studies, never happened, and the sour taste of unprovoked conflict ran as an undercurrent through much of what was to occur in this following period. We have never been afraid to engage in vigorous competition and, if need be, to disagree with groups pursuing the same goals, but would prefer to spend our lives on good terms with our colleagues and competitors, even during periods of controversy. In particular, we would prefer not to work under a charge of being merely derivative workers unwilling to acknowledge the prior discoveries of others, a charge that, at the very least, destroys any joy of discovery. It was hardly an ideal way to start a 30-year project.

Problems with Variability

One matter that demanded early attention with the in vitro cultures was the need to document what cellular events were actually occurring during the 7- to 14-day incubation period during which colonies developed. The cultures in fact had a very heterogeneous appearance. Some colonies contained more than 1,000 cells while other discrete collections of cells contained as few as two to five cells. Individual colonies had a quite different shape and cellular composition that varied from purely granulocytic or macrophage to those with a variable mixture of both cell types. Furthermore, sequential analysis showed that the initiation of cellular proliferation to form colonies was asynchronous—some colonies only initiating days after the cultures were prepared. In addition, the cellular composition of many colonies seemed to change with time, often appearing at first to contain immature cells with ring-shaped nuclei with macrophages appearing later, but coming to dominate colony populations as granulocytic cells matured and died in the colonies.

This heterogeneity of behavior persists today and is now known to be based on the heterogeneity of the cells initiating the various colonies. At the outset however, the cultures seemed highly complex and any phenomenon observable with them might well be due to the operation of more than one biological process.

In different experiments, the overall quality of the colonies could vary widely, and this was properly ascribed to fluctuations in the adequacy of the media or incubating conditions. The large surface area but shallow depth of the cultures and the loosely fitting petri dish lids meant that the cultures readily dried out during incubation, and, to minimize this, it was necessary to use a fully hydrated atmosphere within the incubator. In modern incubators this can still present problems but is usually solved by incorporation of a water bath in the bottom of the incubator, by cutting gas flows to a minimum, and by introducing the gas through the water bath itself, with care to ensure secure seals on the glass inner door of the incubator. In the initial period, we lacked such CO_2 incubators and solved these problems by building gas-tight plastic boxes that could be gassed and then sealed with a container of water inside. This was a cumbersome procedure that limited the numbers of cultures being set up and restricted how frequently the containers could be dismantled for analysis of progress in colony development.

Adequacy of the culture medium was a constant problem that was improved by some curious initial solutions, such as inclusion of trypticase soy broth in the medium, and the addition of extra amounts of amino acids, particularly asparagine. When preselection of fetal calf sera batches became more rigorous, these additions were eventually able to be abandoned.

Our initial publications on bone marrow colonies tended to be dominated by descriptions of the events occurring during colony formation and by attempts to establish some of the basic properties of colony-forming cells.

Much attention was also paid to the cells or tissues that needed to be added to the underlayers to stimulate colony formation. Ray Bradley had initially screened various organs as sources of colony-stimulating activity, settling for a time on trypsinized renal tubule cells as an exotic, but usually active, source of such activity. This was a cumbersome procedure, again restricting the numbers of cultures able to be prepared. In this context, the demonstration by Ichikawa and his colleagues that medium harvested from cultures of various cell lines was active in stimulating colony formation, a finding we confirmed by using various organ-conditioned media, proved to be a major technical advance.

As evident from our publications at this time, we remained very uncertain about the nature of this colony-stimulating activity. We tried ultrafiltration and ultraviolet irradiation of active materials in hopes of minimizing the risk that colony formation was, in fact, based on viral transformation, but the possibility that the active crude materials were merely supplying nonspecific but essential metabolites for the cells could not be eliminated.

The Beginning of Cultures in the Hall Institute

After Ray Bradley and I had worked for some time on colonies he grew in his University laboratory, we decided in 1966 that the time had come for us to attempt to introduce his culture technique into the Hall

The Walter and Eliza Hall Institute, home of our group on the top lighted floor from 1966 to 1986.

Institute. If this was successful, we could then continue our joint studies using material from both laboratories.

This coincided with two major pieces of good fortune for us. Gus Nossal replaced Macfarlane Burnet as the director of the Institute and was to remain an enthusiastic supporter of our work, through all its ups and downs, for the next 31 years. While this was not always visible, because he remained an unrepentant cellular immunologist, his support behind the scenes, where it often mattered, was sustained and effective. He even became an active participant in some of our later experiments when we, for a time, began growing colonies of B lymphocytes.

It was Gus Nossal who decided that our growing skills were being badly impeded by continuing isolation in the remote Animal House.

Almost his first act as director was to move our laboratories to a newly completed floor of the main Hall Institute building. These, to us, palatial quarters were both a pleasure to the eye and nose and purpose-designed for our needs, with not only general-purpose laboratories but with two tissue culture suites and animal rooms conveniently located across the corridor. I have always believed that one needs space if new ideas and enterprises are to be transformed to actions and accomplishments, and we regarded our new space as our most precious resource. Gus Nossal was very much the enthusiastic obstetrician who delivered this untried infant of colonies and factors into the Institute. It was up to us now to demonstrate our value. An enterprising American physician, Bill Robinson, who was undertaking a Ph.D. with us, was given the task of learning the culture technique under instruction from the master in the University and then of trying to reproduce the technique in our own new laboratories.

Despite our better laboratories, we were not often able to reproduce the magnificent colonies grown by Ray Bradley and always remained rather defensive about our inferior product. As it turned out, the very large colonies that became increasingly the focus of Ray's attention and future work are in fact generated by a different set of precursor cells from those generating the more numerous colonies of more modest size. The less mature colony-forming cells forming very large colonies in vitro have a more complex growth factor requirement in contrast to the cells forming more moderate-sized colonies. We would have found ourselves in all manner of trouble trying to characterize CSFs had we settled on a stringent requirement only to work on the biology of these mega-colonies. By good fortune rather than prescience, we settled for cultures that had grown colonies of more modest size as the basis for our future work, taking care to hold back our occasional colonies of very good size should Ray Bradley happen to be paying us a visit.

TWO

Project Goals and Approaches

Casting aside the depressing possibilities that colony formation might be due to viral transformation or to the trivial action of certain metabolites, Bill Robinson and I chose to take the most optimistic view that the colony-stimulating activity being supplied to the cultures by added cells or conditioned medium was in fact a mandatory, tissue-specific physiological regulator of granulocytes and macrophages. This was to remain a hopeful but unverifiable premise throughout almost 20 years of subsequent work.

With fairly acceptable, and not always reliable, cultures we nonetheless felt able to do what I at least had longed to do for years—to begin a search for possible hematopoietic regulators, but now using the marrow cultures as the basic bioassay procedure. The rationale behind the use of this technique was that the cultures did seem to be able not only to detect such a postulated regulator, but to be capable of providing a workable quantitative assay for it because colony numbers and size increased as the content of active material added to the cultures was increased. By counting colony numbers, some quantitative estimate of the amount of active material added seemed possible.

Motivations Behind the Work

Despite our confidence in the importance of agar cultures as a bioassay system and our desire to characterize the CSF, our publications in the next few years are a curious mixture of studies, many of which had little or no apparent bearing on the pursuit of candidate regulatory factors.

The reasons behind this odd behavior were complex. With a decade of work on hematopoiesis behind us, we were faced with a quite novel piece of hematopoietic cell biology and felt obliged to expend considerable effort to characterize what was actually occurring in the cultures and fit it into what was then known about the biology of hematopoietic populations. What were the colony-forming cells and could they be segregated from other marrow cells? What was their appearance? Were they in cell cycle; were they radiosensitive? Were they committed irreversibly to granulocyte and macrophage cell formation? Could they self-renew? Were they the same cells as had recently been characterized in 1961 by Till and McCulloch in Toronto as being able to form giant hematopoietic colonies in the spleen of irradiated recipient mice? Many of our studies in the next decade addressed these questions, slowly building up a hierarchical tree of hematopoietic cells and establishing the interrelationships between these cells and those of comparable cells in other lineages.

With time, we and others developed methods for culturing other types of hematopoietic colonies—eosinophil, megakaryocyte, erythroid, multipotential, and T and B lymphoid. This information slowly became integrated into a working model of the various hematopoietic lineages but had no direct bearing on the project to characterize the CSF for granulocyte and macrophage colony formation.

Today, such an indirect approach to a project would not be countenanced by a group presented with a candidate regulator to investigate. Any workable assay would now suffice and all efforts would be concentrated on purification and cloning, leaving the establishment of the biology to some later date when the purified recombinant molecule was available for passing on to others with expertise in such matters. However, even today, we ourselves would not behave in this latter manner. As medical research workers, we consider it to be of importance to establish the biology behind such regulators and have never been mere pursuers of active molecules. This often makes us uncompetitive, but we believe it to be an important part of our particular role in medical research to understand normal biology and related disease states, not simply to generate reagents.

What is also evident from our publications is that we had a preoccupation with leukemia and kept returning to the question of regulator biology in the special context of leukemic populations. On these occasions, we often moved far away from the narrow path of regulator characterization. The reason for this pattern of behavior is that we were a cancer research unit funded by a cancer society that drew its funds from public donations. We were very conscious of the source of our funding and were determined at all times to work within a framework of defendable relevance to leukemia biology. Again, this made us ill-suited to a single-minded pursuit of regulator molecules, and we strayed repeatedly into complex and time-consuming studies on leukemic patients and leukemic cell models. More than 20 percent of our publications over this 30-year period concerned leukemic cell biology.

One of the curious aspects about the passage of time is the collective loss of memory concerning the actual motivations behind particular pieces of early work. Rereading of these early publications has proved particularly unhelpful in retrieving this information. The discussion sections of the papers are quite restricted to the data being presented and general speculations are nowhere to be found. My memory of these early studies is that, at that time, we did not have as our objective the mass-production of human regulators for clinical use—certainly not for use in the manner in which they would be ultimately used.

What we were initially determined to do in our work on regulators was to purify them and then develop reductionist, unambiguous, bioassay systems that could allow the actions of these regulators to be clearly established—a proof of principle concerning the nature of the regulators and what they might be able to do. Later on, our goals presumably must have changed. From 1980, our papers did refer on occasion to the desirability of mass-producing regulators, but then for possible use as selective suppressing agents in myeloid leukemia. It was only in the mid-1980s, with emerging evidence of the activity of recombinant regulators in vivo, that we began to discuss in our papers the possible more general clinical use of the regulators.

Such limited objectives would now be regarded as somewhat naïve, but the sixties and seventies marked the emergence of hematopoietic biology from the dark ages of vague phenomena, crude uncharacterized materials, and unknown responding tissues. The urge to bring order and certainty out of this chaos was overwhelming.

I cannot believe that, even during this period of monastic generation of light, from 1967 to 1984, we were as completely dismissive of the possible clinical applications of the work in human disease as our publications appear to indicate. Many of us were in fact clinically trained and hoped that patients might one day benefit from our work. I think it was more a question of self-imposed discipline. The prime need was to keep one's head down and get on with the daunting task of bringing order and certainty out of vague chaos. Information before speculation was the unwritten motto, and, even if some of us were word spinners, firm limits were set on what might or might not be appropriate in the discussion sections of our manuscripts.

What this disparate set of motivations resulted in was a very broad approach to the question of CSFs in the framework of emerging hematopoietic and leukemic cell biology. This certainly slowed progress on certain specific questions but turned out eventually to have had many advantages in that, by the time the CSFs were purified, we had a good understanding of their likely role in the body—the converse of the situation with many newer hematopoietic regulators.

Approaches

It needs to be made clear at this point that most of our work on the characterization of hematopoietic regulators was to be performed using inbred mice and cultures of murine cells. There is species specificity with hematopoietic regulators that does, however, allow murine cells to respond to many, but not all, regulators from humans. The advantages in largely restricting such work to the murine species were that it facilitated studies on the biology of hematopoietic populations and, in time, the generation of mice with genetically engineered hypo- and hyperproduction of hematopoietic regulators. There was a hidden disadvantage that only became apparent when patent rights were being contested.

In general, murine work in this field preceded comparable work using human cells and human regulators, a not too surprising situation given the more ready availability of murine tissues for assays or as sources of regulatory factors.

There was in fact some delay in developing the corresponding semi-solid culture system for human granulocyte-macrophage progenitor cells. It was not until 1970 that Beverley Pike and Bill Robinson, then back in Denver, and Michael Paran in Rehovot were able to develop a double-layer culture system, involving the use of peripheral blood cell underlayers or spleen-conditioned medium, that allowed human granulocyte-macrophage colonies of satisfactory quality to be cultured. When this was accomplished, subsequent analyses of human hematopoietic populations revealed that progenitor cell biology is essentially identical in the mouse and man, the only slight disadvantage with human cells being their longer cell cycles and the necessity to use culture periods of two weeks, rather than one week, to obtain more or less comparable colonies.

Certainly in the late 1960s, the murine culture system was the only one available for use in characterizing hematopoietic regulators. Although our initial purification work on the CSF was to be performed using human urine as the source material, it later became evident that the situation regarding tissues with colony-stimulating activity was more complex than we had previously imagined. Resolution of this confusion required careful analysis of many different tissues and, to obtain such tissues in a healthy state, we were forced inevitably to work with murine tissues. There were occasions later when we returned to work with human tissues as source material for assay in both human and murine cultures but, more and more, our work became restricted to the murine system.

At the beginning of attempts to characterize CSF, little information existed on the nature of the cells forming colonies in vitro or where these cells fit in the hierarchy of hematopoietic populations. This information was to emerge during the 1968-1983 period from parallel studies in our laboratories as well as those of many others. None of this information was available to us early in the work on the characterization of hematopoietic regulators, nor did the absence of this information particularly impede the steps initially undertaken.

However, lack of information that clearly was able to be collected is an irresistible force and caused us and others to deviate from our efforts from time to time. On many occasions these fill-in biological experiments were precipitated by delays in the collection of material for biochemical fractionation or the necessary delays during the seven-day assays on such material.

Our laboratories were always very busy places and there was no shortage of projects to undertake when fractionation work was experiencing a lull. In later years with more biochemists involved, the workload of bioassays became continuous, but, human nature being what it is, if some interesting piece of biology was emerging about the hematopoietic populations themselves, this also was pursued with whatever time was available. There were certainly times when multicolored balls were being juggled simultaneously with mounting excitement but perhaps not making an ideal modus operandum for any one of the projects.

THREE

Was the CSF Likely to Be a Regulator?

Rightly or wrongly, in 1967–1968 we believed (and hoped) that the colony-stimulating activity of tissue origin, which was necessary to stimulate granulocyte-macrophage colony formation, might be the genuine regulator of these populations—the analog of the known, but still not fully characterized, regulator for erythroid populations, erythropoietin. We early adopted in the laboratory the working term *colony-stimulating factor* (CSF), for this postulated regulator of granulocyte-macrophage proliferation and assumed naïvely that CSF, like erythropoietin, would be a single regulatory factor.

With this as our working assumption, we felt obliged to establish a body of evidence that would support the proposition that CSF was a bona fide regulator. The prototype regulator, erythropoietin, was by then known to be detectable in the serum and urine, at least under conditions of anemia or hypoxia. If CSF was to be at all comparable, it should also be detectable in serum and urine and presumably in at least some tissue extracts or medium conditioned by such tissues. The latter expectations were indeed already known to be correct from the manner in which bone marrow colony formation had been discovered.

Assays on mouse serum revealed that CSF was detectable in some, but certainly not all, samples from normal mice. The publication of these data in 1967 was the first to use the term *colony-stimulating fac-*

Malcolm Moore, Noel Warner, Don Metcalf, Bill Robinson, and Richard Stanley in 1968.

tor. Given our bias for work on leukemia, we early documented that mice with lymphoid leukemia had elevated levels of CSF in the serum, both in conventional and germ-free animals. This was not particularly surprising to us since we had known for some years that mice with lymphoid leukemia commonly have elevated granulocyte levels—sometimes grossly elevated levels—in the peripheral blood. If indeed CSF was a granulocyte-macrophage regulator, it made sense that mice with elevated granulocyte levels might also have high CSF levels.

Comparable assays on human sera, using murine marrow cultures, produced somewhat similar answers. Sometimes, but not often, CSF was detectable in sera from apparently healthy humans and, rather more often, in sera from patients with leukemia and lymphomas of various types. The activity of human sera was on the whole fairly unimpressive, but there was sufficient activity to keep hopes alive that all was well and that CSF could be present at least sometimes in human serum.

A detailed study of extracts of a wide range of mouse organs revealed CSF to be present in all such extracts and at concentrations that were higher than those in the serum, making a strong indirect case that these organs were in fact producing CSF.

Again, using the logic that CSF levels might be expected to be elevated in situations involving perturbations in granulocyte or macrophage levels, we explored a number of likely situations, most of which involved acute infections, where changes in the numbers of these cells or their function might be anticipated. In humans in the acute stages of mononucleosis, CSF levels were elevated, as they were in mice with experimentally induced infection with the lactate dehydrogenase (LDH)-elevating virus. Studies by others documented comparable elevations in model murine infections and a variety of human infections. Of particular interest and, eventually, importance, was the observation that a single injection of bacterial antigens or bacterial cell-wall lipopolysaccharide (endotoxin) induced massive and rapid rises in serum CSF levels and additional rises also in CSF levels extractable from all organs.

These observations, gathered in the period from 1967 to 1971, represented a substantial indirect body of evidence supporting the view that CSF was likely to be a genuine regulator of granulocyte-macrophage populations. This being so, a case could be made for expending considerable effort to biochemically characterize CSF by purification.

CSF in Mouse Serum

Before most of the supporting evidence had been gathered, we had actually begun attempts to physically characterize CSF. The first source material chosen for CSF characterization was leukemic mouse serum, an appallingly difficult starting material, resulting in data that were greeted with derision by our friendly Israeli competitors. We were advised to get ourselves a decent biochemist to do the work, not the poor Ph.D. student, Richard Stanley, presented with this hopeless task with the assistance of Gordon Ada.

Actually, we had no serious intent to purify CSF from mouse serum. Even in those early days we understood the likely necessity for adequate amounts of starting materials with adequate levels of activity. We were more concerned initially to try to characterize CSF as being macromolecular (i.e., not likely to be a mundane metabolite) and as being protein in nature (and thus, not viral). With these limited objectives, the initial experiments were successful enough in establishing that CSF was indeed likely to be a sizable protein.

It is hard now to imagine a golden period when a project could clearly be worthwhile but where no competitors existed other than presumably our Rehovot counterparts. I kept warning Richard Stanley that this halcyon period could not possibly last and to get on with his experiments. To spur the group to more activity, I even installed a map of the world with pins showing the location of other groups now known to be working on bone marrow cultures. To his credit, this prodding had no impact whatsoever on Richard Stanley.

Human Urine CSF

Never one to be afraid of trying something unusual, Bill Robinson had explored whether CSF was detectable in human urine. It was, and seemed often to be present in higher concentrations in urine from patients with leukemia. Our paper describing these observations was submitted to *Lancet* but was promptly returned because it was thought to be too specialized and better suited for a journal of urology!

Why CSF should regularly be detectable in normal human urine but not normal mouse urine was, and remains, somewhat puzzling. If its presence merely reflected clearance of CSF from the plasma by the kidney, CSF should have been much more convincingly detectable in plasma and serum. We later recognized that lipoproteins in serum can nonspecifically inhibit or kill a wide variety of target cells in bioassays, preventing the cells from responding to stimuli. However this only partly explains the discrepancy.

From the early experiments on bone marrow cultures, renal tubules were a known potent source of CSF and later studies showed that bladder tissue was also a reliable source of CSF. So what did urine CSF represent—cleared circulating CSF or CSF produced locally in the genitourinary tract? If the latter, there might well be something strange or atypical about such urinary CSF. It was certainly difficult to imagine that CSF in the urine would be of much relevance for the stimulation of cell proliferation in the bone marrow.

As always in these early days, we were influenced by what was known about erythropoietin. Erythropoietin was present in human urine, but its credentials as a regulator were nonetheless beyond dispute, even though the presence of erythropoietin in urine would also appear to be inconsequential for an erythropoietic regulator.

Logic therefore suggested that, despite not having the comfort of corresponding credentials for CSF, urinary CSF was probably an acceptable source material for the purification of CSF, just as human urine was beginning to be used for studies on the prototype regulator, erythropoietin.

FOUR

The Purification of CSF from Human Urine

B earing in mind the likely logistical need for plenty of starting material with at least detectable activity, even if the protein content of urine was still significant, we opted to begin our serious efforts to purify CSF using human urine as starting material.

We had access through our Clinical Research Unit to occasional patients with myeloid leukemia and were for a time tempted to restrict our studies to the CSF in leukemic urine. However, few patients with acute leukemia are in a physical or mental state to ensure that their urine is regularly collected for some arcane project involving cultures of mouse bone marrow cells, and they frequently indicated their disinterest by dropping cigarette butts in the samples. Smoking was still permitted in the hospital wards and in the Institute in the late 1960s and our first purification procedure for many urine batches was to remove cigarette butts—hoping we were not inadvertently removing the primary source of CSF.

Ensuring sustained 24-hour urine collections in a busy medical ward was also not a task for which the nursing staff was able to generate much enthusiasm. We were to learn over the years that requests for clinical material from medical or nursing staff, if for research purposes only, were never met with much enthusiasm, despite frequent information-sharing meetings. If the procedures or tests offered something in exchange, such as confirming a diagnosis or, as happened later, offering the possibility of some improvement in patient management, the situation changed dramatically. This was a very understandable set of reactions, but not of much help in the early vague stages of a project.

We eventually decided that attempting to develop a program using leukemic urine, though it potentially would have had a bigger impact on hematologists, was being a little unrealistic. We needed to come back to earth and use what was readily available from normal sources. We did consider for a time collecting urine from schools or army barracks but eventually settled for collections from our staff, both male and, with more difficulty, female. Plastic buckets became a permanent feature of our toilets. To reduce odor and hopefully bacterial contamination possibly leading to degradation of the CSF, sodium azide was added to the buckets. If azide was red-colored, our laboratories must surely have been a distinct pink color, because urine in large volumes became an ever-present accompaniment of daily life. To accelerate our collections, we also briefly considered subsidizing staff visits to the local pub but, after a pilot study on CSF levels in the resulting additional urine, we again retreated to standard sources.

Untreated human urine was toxic for mouse marrow cultures. However, whatever was toxic or inhibitory in urine was removable by dialysis. We therefore settled on a large stainless steel tank with a continuous water flow as the method for dialysing the urine, loading the urine into outsized plastic dialysis tubing in very large sausages. I have never felt quite the same way about sausages since those days.

So began our efforts to purify CSF. I did the necessary bioassays, assisted by two technical assistants. The responsibility for protein separation and purification fell on Richard Stanley's shoulders with the eventual help of two technical assistants. I could certainly offer no technical advice to Richard and, in the Institute, there was nobody with experience in separative protein chemistry. Informed advice needed to be obtained from adjacent institutes if problems arose.

What none of us realized was that purifying CSF from any source in the late 1960s was an impossible technical feat. Until CSF was purified, there was no way of knowing how much CSF was actually needed to stimulate a culture. If the specific activity of CSF was high, or extremely high as turned out to be the case, then what was detectable in urine was an exceedingly minute amount of protein. Two consequences flowed from such a situation. First, a tremendous volume of urine would need to be purified to obtain even a minute amount of purified material. Second, the vast majority of the protein molecules in the starting material would not be CSF and, as contaminating proteins, would need to be separated away, requiring a fold-purification of some frightening order of magnitude.

To form an idea of the nature of this problem, it is useful to compare two situations. Albumin constitutes approximately 60 percent of all protein in the serum. To purify this albumin only requires, in principle, a less than twofold purification, although the job in fact is far tougher than this simple calculation implies because, to obtain absolute purity, minute amounts of all manner of protein molecules must still be meticulously separated. Nevertheless, obtaining reasonably pure albumin is not a particularly overwhelming task. We now know that fewer than 1 in 100,000 protein molecules in urine is actually a CSF molecule. To obtain pure CSF required therefore a 100,000-fold purification and, with the column fractionation methods available in the 1960s, the lack of specific antibodies that might be used for affinity column purification or any particularly novel properties of CSF molecules, the task of CSF purification was essentially beyond existing technical methods. It was not until the late 1970s, when high-performance liquid chromatography was adapted for work with proteins, that purification folds of the order needed could then be achieved.

Sometimes it is a comfort not to know the worst at the outset, otherwise projects would never be commenced. This in no way diminishes the chronic frustration of limping, inadequate progress, but slow progress did occur, which, at the time, was a source of pride of accomplishment.

The protein nature of CSF became firmly established in early work from its large apparent molecular weight (>10,000), its heat lability, and resistance to UV irradiation but degradation by proteases.

The General Purification Strategy

Purification of an unknown protein is a project that has two distinct phases. In the initial phase, specific questions are asked about the properties of the molecule under study. Does it bind, or not bind, to a particular column matrix? Is it a sticky or nonsticky molecule? What is its apparent size or electrical charge? These are the properties that distinguish one molecule from another and the information forms the basis for formal attempts to purify the molecule. This is in fact a happy time in a project as all answers are of interest, particularly if repetition shows the answers to be confirmable. Such experiments are generating nice data that can be presented in a satisfying figure, but they are only preliminary moves in a purification project.

In the second phase, progressive purification requires a correct *sequence* of purification steps to be devised. Attempts to construct such a sequence can be extremely frustrating and lead to many technical dead-ends. A particular step may remove major amounts of contaminating protein but potentially can lead to future problems. Sometimes, the sequence of such steps needs to be reversed or additional steps inserted to reduce the overall load of protein being handled. Constructing a workable sequence can become a frustrating nightmare where little information that is novel is being accrued and continued losses of valuable material become depressing.

We learned painfully that the production of new batches of starting material needs to be continuous in such projects, as does processing these batches through at least some established steps, so that material at a certain stage of purification was always available as backup material to replace that lost in some further fractionation attempt. We were also to learn the painful truth that the purer the product, the more prone it became to devastating and unexplained loss—usually by adsorption to glass or plastic surfaces.

All of us had to learn to accept gracefully continuous frustration and disasters—not to assign blame to anyone but to counter adversity as best we could, often with black humor. It comes as no surprise that not all were equally successful in handling chronic adversity and there were on occasions some spectacular temper tantrums.

The procedure adopted for urinary CSF purification was therefore to make test fractionation runs using columns containing various gel materials that were capable of segregating proteins passing through them into rough layers according to their size, surface charge, or stickiness—properties that distinguish proteins one from another. Proteins differ also in their solubility in the presence of high salt concentrations, which was a particularly useful method for an initial bulk fractionation step to remove unwanted proteins.

Our laboratories became filled progressively with various glass columns containing a variety of materials we hoped would be able to separate CSF from other urinary proteins. Material to be processed was fed into the tops of the columns and then over the next one or two days, the material gradually layered out in the columns and began running out the exit at the bottom of the columns. The various fractions were then captured in sequence in a series of small test tubes in a circular or linear array with the next tube advanced every minute or two by an electrically timed motor.

For a long time we were worried by the possibility that proteins might become degraded either by contaminating proteolytic enzymes or for physical reasons if the columns were allowed to run for periods of days at room temperature. At first, therefore, we ran all fractionation columns in glass-fronted refrigerators, further consuming laboratory space, or in cold rooms. It was some time before we became confident enough that work at room temperature was in fact satisfactory for CSF purifications and that such precautions are not often required for proteins of this general type. The risk of microbial contamination and degradation of precious protein was reduced by inclusion of sodium azide in all materials being fractionated. Azide is highly lethal—more so than cyanide—and, with the busy traffic in our laboratories and changing technical staff, it is slightly astonishing that in 20 years no accidental poisoning occurred. I trust that our record will continue.

The Purification of Urinary CSF

The project to purify CSF from human urine made good initial progress in establishing valuable information about the basic properties of this molecule. Clearly CSF was macromolecular with an apparent

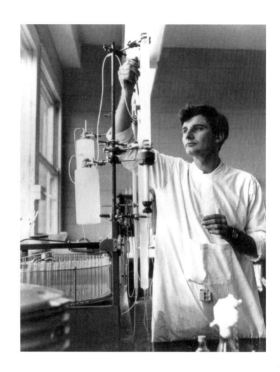

Richard Stanley fractionating
human urine CSF in 1969.

molecular weight from zone sedimentation experiments of approximately 45,000 but with a somewhat larger apparent size from gel filtration experiments. Separation by gradient gel electrophoresis also indicated a molecular weight of approximately 45,000 and we settled on
this as our estimate of the size of human urinary CSF.

With time, the project settled on the sequential use of diethyla-
minoethyl (DEAE) cellulose chromatography, calcium phosphate chromatography, then again a DEAE cellulose step followed by Biogel
filtration. Sequences of this type slowly began to yield small amounts
of fairly highly purified material.

This progress began to generate discussions on the manner in which
we might be able to certify material as having been fully purified. In the
early 1970s, definitions of purity for a protein were rather vague. As
judged by the documentation used in studies accepted for publication
at that time, certification of purity seemed to require no more than that
the material produced a single band when stained with Coomassie blue
after separation by electrophoresis in a native gel or preferably a gradi-

ent gel and that this band contained all the biological activity. Single bands on polyacrylamide electrophoresis were able to be generated by our best urinary CSF preparations, but these bands were rather broad. Did this indicate the persistence of contaminating proteins or was it merely the result of a variable content of carbohydrate, rendering the material rather heterogeneous in size? The material had been purified approximately 1,000-fold and further progress was going to require the development of some additional separation procedures.

Human urinary CSF was susceptible to degradation by proteolytic enzymes but was relatively resistant compared with other proteins. Accordingly, a further step of protein digestion was added to the purification sequence. Although this resulted in loss of two-thirds of the CSF, it did achieve a considerable 50-fold further enrichment. Evidence that CSF might also contain carbohydrate had been mounting and when the highly enriched CSF was treated with a carbohydrate-splitting enzyme, the existence of the carbohydrate was confirmed. This was eventually to allow the use of plant lectin columns, particularly concanavalin A-Sepharose, able to bind carbohydrate-containing proteins to achieve factor enrichment. When polyacrylamide gel electrophoresis was added as a final purification step, minute amounts of CSF preparations were obtained that we estimated to have been purified 100,000-fold. This stage had been reached by 1972 but the amounts of enriched CSF, arguably purified to homogeneity, that had been produced were vanishingly small.

The feat of purifying human urinary CSF had possibly been achieved but the amounts achieved permitted only a very limited number of precious in vitro experiments. The purification project began to lose momentum.

Almost from the beginning of the purification project we had been hoping to obtain enough relatively pure urinary CSF to inject into mice to determine whether any observable change in granulocyte or monocyte populations could be induced. However, we were very wary of engaging in such a study that would clearly be open to critical comment. There had been a long history of investigators injecting mice with crude materials and claiming the induction of responses in the injected animals. These ranged from rapid release of mature granulocytes to the blood to more sustained elevations of blood white cell levels. By and large, these earlier studies did not result in reproducible phenomena that encouraged study by others. One exception was the bacterial cell wall component, endotoxin, which was obviously capable on injection of inducing a number of changes in white cell levels and spleen size. Clearly, anything injected by us, if producing responses, needed to be free of the criticisms either that it was junk material or that contaminating endotoxin was responsible.

In 1968 Ray Bradley had in fact performed a detailed study on the effect of injecting unpurified CSF-containing material in the form of unfractionated embryo-conditioned medium. The control material injected was incubated medium or medium incubated with thymus tissue adjusted to have a similar protein content, but with no detectable CSF. The CSF-containing material was observed to produce a slow selective rise in granulocyte levels in the blood, without altering colony-forming cell numbers in the marrow but causing a 10-fold rise in these cells in the spleen and, intriguingly, an almost 100-fold rise in these cells in the blood. This latter finding was to become forgotten during the following 20 years but was then to re-emerge as one of the most dramatic consequences of CSF treatment.

This 1968 pilot study had intrigued us and finally tempted us in 1971 to inject a single dose of urine CSF, by then enriched 100-fold into neonatal and adult mice. The dose of CSF injected was approximately 100 ng. The neonatal mice developed a two- to threefold rise in neutrophils and monoytes, maximal two days after injection, but the adult mice showed merely a twofold rise in monocyte levels. No significant change was observed in colony-forming cell levels in the marrow. Subtle changes were observed, involving a more rapid entry of newly formed granulocytes into the blood of the adult mice and a curious shortening of the lag period that colony-forming cells from the CSF-injected mice required before commencing division in culture. These changes were suggestive that some in vivo response might have occurred but were on the whole discouraging, even though we had probably used only a homeopathic dose of CSF. Our exercise was a momentary rush of blood to the head. We were to shy away from any further attempts to inject CSF into mice for a further 14 years until we were better prepared with pure CSF and in quantity.

One matter of increasing concern to us during our purification studies was the type of marrow-derived colonies being stimulated by our progressively more pure urinary CSF. If our usual colonies were not of Bradley standard in size or number when stimulated by various crude conditioned media, the colonies stimulated by urinary CSF were even more miserable in size. Even today, colonies stimulated by urinary CSF are small and temperamental in their development—so much so, that we still routinely use urinary CSF as one of the standard stimuli in testing new batches of fetal calf serum for their adequacy. If test fetal calf serum supports colonies of reasonable size when stimulated by urinary CSF, then such serum almost certainly will support good colony formation in response to virtually any other stimulus.

One of the very curious aspects about human urinary CSF that also became apparent was that it was quite unable to stimulate colony formation by human bone marrow cells. Some small clusters did develop, but no colonies—a finding that was completely disconcerting. Years later it was found that if agarose is substituted for agar in the medium, somewhat better colonies do develop. Later it was also found that good colonies can be stimulated if this CSF is supplemented by a small concentration of another CSF (GM-CSF), but the inactivity of human urine CSF on what should be its appropriate target cell population remains unexplained.

While we had learned to ignore misgivings about the consistently poor size of urinary CSF-stimulated colonies, what could not be ignored was the fact that the colonies in no way resembled the original Bradley-type colonies in composition. Most seven-day colonies were composed merely of macrophages, and no large granulocytic or granulocyte-macrophage colonies were being stimulated. While it could be postulated that some cofactor was now missing from the cultures that was necessary to allow granulocytic colonies to develop, a radically different alternative was emerging as a more likely possibility. We had begun this project assuming that there was but one type of CSF. What if this was incorrect and there were other types of CSF, some able to stimulate granulocytic colony formation? The crude materials in use in the 1960s might well have contained multiple types of CSF.

Two sets of observations in 1971 made the deficiencies regarding urinary CSF much more obvious and not able to be dismissed by some vague explanation that our general culture procedures may have progressively become worse over the years. I had begun working on the response of mice to the injection of the bacterial-derived antigen, flagellin, and the bacterial cell-wall-derived lipopolysaccharide, endotoxin. Injection of either material into mice produced a dramatic 1,000-fold rise in serum CSF levels within three hours and use of such sera to stimulate bone marrow cultures produced very large granulocytic, granulocyte-macrophage, and macrophage colonies entirely comparable with the original colonies grown by Bradley. Clearly there was nothing wrong with our general culture technique or media. In the second set of experiments, a new Ph.D. student, John Sheridan, had begun examining the CSF content of various mouse organs and their capacity to produce CSF when cultured. Many of these extracts or conditioned media had only moderate activity and the colonies were small and composed of macrophages. However, some were highly active and again stimulated the formation of both granulocytic and macrophage colonies.

The mounting disenchantment with the biological properties of urinary CSF coincided with Richard Stanley becoming transformed from a student to a more independent postdoctoral staff member. By chance, at this time, in a bizarre episode involving a usually meticulous technician, our entire supply of highly purified urinary CSF was thrown away by accident during a routine clean-out of the outdated fractionation samples accumulating in our refrigerators. It seemed that fate was telling us to abandon further work with urinary CSF. We had taken the project about as far as was feasible at the time and the product was hardly impressive in its biological activities.

Richard Stanley became more interested in parallel work with Ray Bradley, fractionating highly active CSF-containing material from the pregnant mouse uterus. This murine-derived CSF seemed able to produce much larger colonies than did human urine CSF, although again most colonies were composed of macrophages.

Our work on human urine CSF essentially ceased in 1973 with the departure of Richard Stanley for a postdoctoral period of five years at the Ontario Cancer Institute, Toronto. Working fairly much alone, he did round off the story of human urinary CSF for publication, then proceeded to the purification of mouse L-cell-derived CSF, completing this latter project at the Albert Einstein Medical School in New York in 1977.

Human urine CSF dropped out of our CSF program because we agreed not to proceed further with this molecule, passing the work over to Richard Stanley on his departure for Toronto at the end of 1972. This type of voluntary restraint, in favor of a departing colleague who we had come to regard with much affection, was only slightly unusual 25 years ago. In today's competitive world, such behavior would be regarded as being fairly stupid. Furthermore, the information gathered on this CSF would be regarded as the intellectual property of the Institute and not free for casual disposal to a departing colleague. At the time, however, the actual situation was that we did not have the resources to work on multiple fronts and other CSF work was becoming more appealing. We did in fact work briefly in 1978 with a CSF being produced by mouse yolk sacs as part of an analysis of hematopoiesis in fetal life. This was probably a form of M-CSF but the limited availability of starting material prevented the analysis from being extended too far.

As was found to be the case with the other CSFs, the degree of purification achieved for the L-cell-derived CSF by 1977 was possibly not sufficient to allow amino acid sequencing. Richard Stanley later developed a more stringent purification procedure including adsorption and elution of this CSF from receptor-bearing target cells and it was superpurified material of this quality that was later to provide usable amino acid sequence data.

Our human urine CSF purification project had produced a highly purified product but one that would require much further effort by Richard Stanley and his colleagues in Canada and the United States to achieve purification to homogeneity. It had, however, been a project that taught us much about the procedures required for protein purification and the necessity for tight teamwork where continuous bioassays were required to monitor purification.

A Confusion of Terminologies

Work on the CSF able to stimulate the formation of colonies of granulocytes and/or macrophages had begun with the naïve assumption that there was only a single active agent, a neat counterpart of the erythroid stimulating factor, erythropoietin. Until the end of the 1960s, the literature being published on the subject reflected this simple notion.

Thereafter, and throughout the 1970s, matters began to become much more complicated, and this is reflected in the literature of the 1970s in which a confusion of terminologies began to appear.

In hematology meetings, a convention arose that if one was working with crude unfractionated material, one simply referred to "colony-stimulating activity" (CSA). If the material was partially or possibly fully purified, it was then proper to refer to the material as "colony-stimulating factor" (CSF). The only consistent dissenters from this convention were the Rehovot group, who preferred the term "macrophage-granulocyte inducer" (MGI).

This convention worked well enough until it became increasingly apparent that the CSF being worked with from different tissue sources appeared to have different physical properties, particularly different sizes.

At this stage the source began to need to be mentioned to avoid confusion, resulting in such descriptive terms as human urine CSF or L-cell CSF, mouse uterus CSF, or mouse lung-conditioned-medium CSF. This was becoming very cumbersome, yet some method was necessary to distinguish between the various types of preparation.

For a time, we used an acronym subscript, such as CSF_{MLCM} or CSF_{HU}, to simplify matters. At some stage in the mid-1970s we even began to use the terminology $GM\text{-}CSF_{MLCM}$, etc., I suppose on the valid enough grounds that all the various materials did in fact stimulate some granulocyte or macrophage colony formation, even if the relative frequencies of the different colony types varied widely.

Any reader who tries to relate this terminology to present-day terminology must certainly be bewildered. In 1976 a small international workshop was held to try to standardize the techniques of bone marrow culture and some of the nomenclature being used not only for the clonogenic cells but also the active CSFs of various types. Unlike the cabal of immunologists who introduced an interleukin terminology (IL-1, IL-2, etc.) then enforced it, hematologists proved to be unrepentant individualists. Ernie McCulloch from Toronto, never one to withhold his opinions, declared that he might consider sharing his wife with others, but never his toothbrush or his terminology.

There was a very real biological problem behind this confusion. Until amino acid sequence data were obtained from various CSFs, there was no way of determining whether or not all forms of CSF contained a common polypeptide chain. The larger CSFs might simply be dimeric or trimeric forms of one basic polypeptide chain, with any remaining size difference not quite fitting such a possibility then being ascribable to variable amounts of carbohydrate.

From 1971 we had begun to document and publish the relative frequencies of granulocyte, granulocyte-macrophage, and macrophage colonies developing after stimulation by different types of CSF-containing material. The relative proportions of these various colonies did change in a concentration-dependent manner, but, nevertheless, there were overriding differences according to the source of the CSF.

Although we could not justify it on biochemical grounds, we began to form the view that it would make more sense to reclassify CSF subtypes using a nomenclature that described the predominant colony types stimulated by the material. For example, the CSF from human urine, pregnant mouse uterus, yolk sac, or L-cells dominantly stimulated macrophage colony formation, and we began to apply the acronym M-CSF to such material. Material stimulating both types of colony we began to refer to as GM-CSF.

It was not until in a review we wrote in 1978 that we settled on the use of this terminology. A granulocyte-active material, which had been recently described in peritoneal cell-conditioned medium by Horiuchi and Ichikawa, we provisionally termed G-CSF. We of course tried to carry logic too far, coining other acronyms like EO-CSF and Meg-CSF. These latter did not survive, for EO-CSF was to become IL-5 and the Meg-CSF being referred to actually did not exist but was in fact part of the biological activity of IL-3 (Multi-CSF).

However, M-CSF, GM-CSF, and G-CSF were to survive to the present time as the usual names for these particular factors. Our hunch that differences based on functional activity were likely to be the correct manner to distinguish the various CSFs was much later to be proved valid when amino acid sequencing and cDNA cloning were to reveal that these CSFs had entirely different polypeptide moieties and were encoded by distinct genes. While we were probably more experienced than others by this stage, our decision to assume that functional activity was the key to resolving the confusion with the CSFs was probably good luck rather than superior wisdom.

When Richard Stanley completed his purification of CSF from L-cell-conditioned medium in 1977, he described it as CSF-1, being, in his view, the first CSF to be arguably purified. It was certainly the first CSF to be subjected to sustained efforts at purification but publication of his data was actually in a later issue of the same journal in which we described the equivalent purification of GM-CSF from mouse lung-conditioned medium. We were not therefore impressed by his terminology and preferred our own.

In the remainder of this account I will use the terminology currently used for the CSFs although the reader cross-checking information in the original papers will be left as confused by the 1970s literature as those of us actually were in the 1970s when more and more, apparently differing, CSFs were being encountered.

FIVE

The Dubious Joys of Bioassays

We began our biochemical work on the purification of CSF from human urine as novices in a world of unforeseen technical problems. Our decision to monitor such purification steps using colony formation as the quantitative bioassay was to lock us into a demanding routine for 15 years in which little could be taken for granted except the continuing workload involved.

At first, fractionation experiments generating samples for bioassay were episodic and not too disruptive of other experiments. However, these were early days and, with time, necessary bioassays became more frequent and more and more demanding. At the stage when several biochemists were generating fractions on a virtually daily basis, the resulting workload for the two biological technicians preparing the assay cultures and for me with the job of scoring them became heavy indeed and continued at this level for more than a decade. It would have helped if the bioassay cultures were always of dependable quality, but in culture work nothing is entirely predictable and we were to run foul of some very odd occurrences that often made it very difficult to produce answers of value to our biochemical colleagues.

A single column fractionation might generate up to 100 or 150 tubes of consecutive fractions, any one of which (or, more hopefully, a dozen or so consecutive tubes) might contain the CSF being processed. It would

Sue Stevens preparing marrow cultures for bioassaying
CSF fractions 1972.

be a disaster if all fractions contained equal amounts of CSF, indicating
some total technical failure of the separation procedure, and equally disastrous if none contained CSF because the column had presumably irreversibly trapped the CSF molecules. Which of these outcomes had
resulted could only be established by bioassaying each column fraction.
To reduce the workload, because duplicate cultures always had to be used
and often active fractions had to be tested at multiple concentrations,
bioassays were usually limited to every second or third fraction.

The necessity for a seven-day bioassay to establish which fractions
contained CSF was a perpetual irritation for the various biochemists
who ended up working on CSF purification. I could only counter this
irritation by pointing out that, with multiple batches always undergoing
one or another type of fractionation, work was never actually impeded
by this mandatory wait. Sometimes, however, anxiety levels reached
such proportions that I would break house rules and attempt an early
scoring of cultures to provide at least a provisional answer on where the
activity was running. I did not like this preliminary peeping because

the culture dish lids often were covered with condensed water from the super-saturated atmosphere in the incubator. This impaired a clear view of the contents of the culture and was not helped by the much smaller size of the half-developed colonies. Interim scoring almost certainly guaranteed some contamination of the cultures because the condensed water on the culture lids often ran in under the loose-fitting lids into the culture itself. It was also not uncommon to knock the trays, breaking the delicate gels, or even on occasion to drop such culture trays during this maneuver, which definitely pleased no one.

Even the preliminary preparation of column fractions for bioassay was not a procedure for the indolent or weak-willed. The sixties and seventies were before the era of the routine availability of disposable Millipore filters for sterilizing each sample. The Millipore filters then in use were composed of three metal pieces and a plastic ring together with a disposable Millipore membrane. The various parts were washable and reusable after reassembly with a new Millipore filter with subsequent autoclaving, but frequently the components were reassembled slightly imperfectly and valuable specimens often leaked out or failed to be adequately filtered. Contamination of some specimens was usual in any experiment involving 50 to 100 fractions. Such contamination often seemed to involve the active fractions containing CSF, but I was never motivated to subject this firm belief to statistical analysis.

Most fractions commonly needed some subsequent treatment steps such as dialysis to remove toxic amounts of azide or buffer solutions, adding enormously to the technical workload represented by even a single column fractionation run.

To convey the effort involved in these repetitive series of procedures properly, it suffices to say that, in the bioassays monitoring the purification of one CSF alone, a quarter of a million assay cultures were required, and this was not an exceptional example. As it was my job to score most of these cultures, I came to hate certain fractionation procedures such as DEAE-cellulose where almost every fraction could contain some activity and, in contrast, to love size-based gel filtration fractionations where only a handful of cultures were actually positive. One became adept at scanning and discarding negative cultures when a typical day might involve scoring 800 or more such cultures in addition to whatever else was in progress that day.

Titration curves of the activity of various material containing CSF showed that the dose-response curve was sigmoid. Below a critical concentration, no colonies developed in the culture, then, as concentrations increased, low numbers of small colonies developed. This number increased in a log/linear manner until plateau numbers of colonies developed, beyond which increasing CSF concentrations resulted in little more than an increase in colony size.

All scoring of cultures was performed on unstained petri dish cultures, and it rapidly became apparent that monitoring colony numbers was the only practical method for scoring such cultures. To pick off colonies and somehow establish their content of cells (from 50 to more than 2,000) was a nightmarish impracticality. The variability in colony size within any one dish also made us very wary about applying some indirect method such as thymidine uptake in cultured cell suspensions to monitor cell proliferation. This system would have worked well enough but would have been slower and much more expensive. Furthermore, a major reason for working with colonies was that one could more accurately interpret what was happening at the individual clonogenic cell level, with all its heterogeneity. This very heterogeneity and its cellular basis proved to be of critical importance later in recognizing the existence of more than one type of CSF.

Persons scoring cultures therefore had to learn how to recognize a clonal population of more than 50 cells in a living culture and reach this decision quickly and with consistency. Most biologists became able fairly quickly to perform this minor feat and produce relatively consistent answers on colony counts in the dish. This is actually not a trivial accomplishment. Some colonies contain widely dispersed cells while, conversely, tightly packed colonies can appear deceptively small, and the inexpert always missed both types of colonies. It became a matter of self-training, by picking off colonies then staining them with orcein, to learn from the stained colonies what 50 cells can actually look like if loosely dispersed or tightly packed.

Colony counts were performed using a battlement-style pattern moving up and down over a ruled matrix of squares using some consistent rule for dealing with colonies lying astride the ruled reference lines. There was also need to be particularly careful about focusing up and down continuously. The cultures are three-dimensional, potentially with colonies at all depths in the culture. At 35x magnifications these 1-mm deep cultures were not excessively difficult to score provided focusing was continuous, although after six or so hours, wrists did tend to become sore if the focusing knob had stiffened. The edges of these culture were particularly rich in colonies partly because of the centrifugal motion used in mixing the cells for culture with the added stimulus before gelling occurred and partly because of the added depth of the cultures at the dish edge due to a meniscus effect. This was not helped by the fact that the optical image with the curved mirror transmitting the light through the culture changed from white on black to black on white at the very edges.

This counting procedure, although sounding complex, in fact is not an excessively difficult task once one has had some practice. All observers tend to drift with time in what they are scoring as colonies and back-reference to cultures initially scored can correct this observer drift. There were occasional people who just could not manage this process of maintaining attention. Their colony counts became bizarre after 50 or more cultures, and to point this out and demonstrate the inanity of their counts had no effect. They simply were incapable of sustained concentration and had to be given other work to perform.

Even though I had a few irate letters from technicians in other countries, I stand by what I wrote in a textbook on this technique about the scoring of colonies. This is not work for a technical assistant. It is a job requiring constant attention and watchfulness—watchfulness for technical faults or, more important, unusual and potentially novel phenomena. It makes an enormous difference if one's scientific reputation and career depend on a perceptive analysis of a culture. This is potentially at issue when every culture dish is examined and has a marvelous effect on focusing the mind.

For reasons that still elude me, even the most careful colony count on an unstained culture is an underestimate of what is actually present when the intact culture is floated onto a glass slide, dried, and stained. However, such underestimates parallel actual colony numbers quite closely, allowing counts from unstained cultures still to be used as a valid enough series of comparative counts.

There are minimum and maximum limits to how many bone marrow cells can be used to initiate a culture. Colony counts and titration curves become ambiguous if a maximum of only five or ten colonies develop in a culture. Conversely, if more than 100 colonies develop in a culture, accurate colony counts become difficult because colonies tend to overlap each other. To standardize our assay cultures as best we could, despite the ever-present fluctuations in how well colonies grew on a particular day, we not only standardized our fetal calf serum by careful pretesting of batches to always use equivalent batches, but also fixed on using marrow cells from a pool of femurs from C57BL mice aged two to three months. There are strain variations in the number and types of colony-forming cells present in a murine marrow population, thus C57BL mice were chosen because of their average frequencies of such cells and the broad range of colony types and size able to be generated by these cells.

Even once routine procedures had been settled on for the assay of biochemical samples, and even with the diligence of experienced biological technicians preparing the assay cultures, it was common enough for small catastrophes to occur. From time to time, batches of fetal calf serum or medium would become contaminated. Less frequently a failure of CO_2 supplies to the incubators or incubator breakdowns would occur. These were correctable enough, once identified, but did require a repetition of all experiments that had been affected. The biologists in the group had to accept the blame for such failures, repeat the work, and thereafter keep an even more watchful eye on possible sources of trouble.

These minor catastrophes are familiar enough to anyone who has done such tissue culture work and caused little more than occasional exasperation. There were, however, several periods of prolonged and seemingly inexplicable disasters that were to sorely try our patience and capacity for finding an explanation.

After some years of bioassay work, despite minor fluctuations in the quality of our cultures, we had formed a clear idea of what were acceptable colony counts in our standard cultures containing 75,000 maximally stimulated bone marrow cells. "Acceptable" for assays on CSF were cultures producing 50 to 120 colonies in cultures being maximally stimulated, although we preferred tighter limits of 100 to 120.

There were three sustained occasions, however, when, for no obvious reason, maximum colony numbers fell as low as 10 to 20, making assays unsatisfactory. Every possible source of variability was carefully cross-checked—media errors, abnormal bottles of fetal calf serum (which were often not uniformly mixed prior to bottling by the suppliers)—but no obvious explanation emerged.

In two of these episodes of sustained disaster, mysteriously some cultures were fine and others virtually devoid of colonies in the same experiments. The confusion and frustration of these bizarre occurrences were to go on for months before the causes were finally traced. In the first, we had been using plastic buckets as receptacles for used glass pipettes. This had led to some, but not all, pipettes becoming toxic. Even after careful washing, reuse of these pipettes still was able to add something toxic to the cultures. This was finally shown to be due to the use of toxic filler material in the manufacture of the plastic buckets and was solved by switching to stainless steel containers.

In the second episode, the cause was finally found to be variable toxicity of the plastic culture dishes used for the cultures. In the manufacturing process, batches of 20 petri dishes were placed in plastic packets then sterilized by adding the gas ethylene dioxide. These packets were then supposed to be stored by the manufacturer for three months before sale to allow degassing of the toxic gas to occur from the sealed plastic packets. Despite denials, the U.S. manufacturer had run short of supplies and provided us with newly produced packets that had not been allowed to degas. Because supplies tended to be irregular, we had ordered a very large number of cartons of these packages representing some 25,000 culture dishes. These were the defective culture dishes causing our troubles. We were devastated to realize that this massive batch was unusable but nevertheless stored them in our plant room and forgot about them. When the explanation of their toxicity was finally determined, we were later vastly relieved to be able to use the offending boxes after their long period of storage in disgrace. Shortly thereafter, we decided that a local producer would be more satisfactory and helped to establish an Adelaide manufacturing facility for these petri dishes, ensuring that irradiation was used to sterilize the packets.

We were still left with a third unresolved puzzle as to why, during certain years, colony numbers could fluctuate in apparently standardized cultures of C57BL mouse cells. We even went to the length of plotting daily maximal colony numbers on a calendar mounted length-

wise along the corridor wall. It became obvious that astonishing fluctuations slowly occurred over periods of weeks from grossly subnormal
to quite acceptable colony numbers. There were no episodes of infection in the animal rooms and no variations in the diet being fed the
mice. We did notice, however, that marrow cells taken from mice coming from the detached Animal House on the other side of the hospital
did produce acceptable and uniform numbers of colonies at times when
marrow cells from mice in the main building did not. The detached
Animal House was a conventional "dirty" facility and presumably was
much more subject to incidental epidemics. We wondered whether
recurrent minor infections were needed to generate "normal" numbers
of colony-forming cells in mice, although our work with germ-free
mice made this unlikely, because germ-free mice have normal numbers
of colony-forming cells in their marrow.

There are times when biology has aspects of black magic and if
Animal House mice were "lucky," might our main stock of mice
behave in a more "normal" or predictable manner if they were first
housed for a month or so in this Animal House? We tried this and the
maneuver was successful. Our C57BL mice after a sojourn in the
Animal House now generated reproducible numbers of colonies. Why
this was so is an unresolved puzzle, but desperate needs call for desperate remedies and for the next couple of years this peculiar procedure
was used. It was not without some risk because mice from the detached
Animal House could not be reintroduced under any circumstances into
the clean rooms of our newer laboratories. However, cell suspensions
could be brought back if care was taken with their subsequent disposal
and that of the cultures. The technicians learned to put up with this
inconvenience of the long daily journey to collect marrow cells and
their subsequent inability to enter our own animal rooms until after a
quarantine period.

These episodes have been described to illustrate that bioassays done
to monitor biochemical fractions were always at risk of failure. When
coupled with equivalent risks of error and failure in biochemical fractionation procedures, progress at times was scarcely apparent even to
the most optimistic.

The final reason for the fluctuating progress of CSF purification and
a major reason why the project took a total of 15 years was the very

length of the project. This project passed through a succession of hands as Ph.D. students, postdocs, and technicians came and went during the period. With each departure, the level of expertise fell and momentum was lost until sufficient experience was obtained to again begin making slow progress. In my more gloomy phases, I saw the CSF purification project as a giant toothed saw with little peaks of achievement being surely followed by troughs and lost ground. This situation did not change until more permanent biochemical staff joined the group.

It became necessary to settle on some unit of measure for CSF. Tests showed that observed titers of CSF were not dependent on the absolute numbers of marrow cells cultured or on the maximum number of colonies developing. Because absolute numbers of colonies did vary from time to time for the reasons recounted, we settled on a unit scale where 50 U/ml was the CSF concentration able to stimulate half-maximal numbers of colonies to develop, whatever the actual maximal colony numbers were on that day. This unit system worked very well in practice and eventually had the felicitous outcome that, for a number of regulators, 1 mg of regulator was equivalent to 10^8 such units. This meant that 50 U/ml was actually a concentration of about 250 pg/ml (less than one part in a million), giving a reason why concentrations of CSF were so low in tissues and serum and why the task of purification was so formidable.

On Personal Involvement

It might seem surprising, or at least a possible waste of expert time, for the head of a growing research unit to spend long periods on most days scoring assay cultures of fractionation runs that often were many-fold repeats of earlier identical fractionation experiments or routine tests on the reagents and culture media being used. Why do it and why do it for 15 years? I had two reasons behind my actions. First, I have never regarded any set of cultures as "routine." Apart from the constant necessity to keep a watchful eye on the quality of the cultures and the precision with which replicate cultures did actually match, such cultures were each in essence actual experiments in which novel colonies or phenomena might occur. This in fact happened fairly regularly and

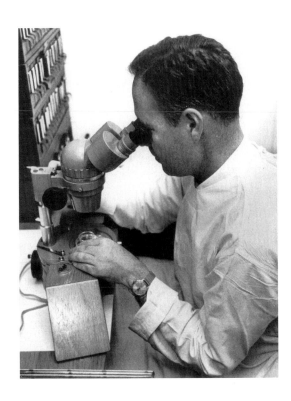

Don Metcalf scoring
bioassays on CSF fractions
in 1973.

led to the discovery of several novel hematopoietic regulators. Furthermore, any culture dish is a highly complex pattern resulting from the simultaneous occurrence of many phenomena. It was only after these patterns became repeatedly registered that questions about the biology of what was being looked at began to emerge and lead to exploratory side experiments, some of considerable relevance. In one sense, much of the counting could have been performed almost as quickly by skilled technicians, but such technicians were better employed preparing new cultures at which they were much more reliable and precise than I could ever have hoped to be.

For projects lasting 5 to 10 years, it did not seem appropriate to pass the tedious scoring of cultures over to some unfortunate student as a chore to be performed rather than letting the student engage in some shorter-term independent experiments. Moreover, I felt that if I genuinely wanted progress to be achieved in what was clearly going to be a long-term project, and if this progress was going to be maintained and finally successful, despite the tedium involved, it was the least I could do to pull my weight in the project by generating the assay data. It is my experience that teams work well on difficult, sustained, and at times depressing projects if everyone, including the team leader, is clearly carrying an equal burden.

I value happy teamwork at least as highly as achieving results and the daily chores of assay scoring seemed a small price to be paying for a group that had pride in its work and was happy to provide mutual assistance when workloads became unbalanced. Perhaps I might have achieved more if I had spent more time reading or thinking, but, so far as I was concerned, seniority was of no relevance in the project. All were equally dependent on one another and I would cheerfully have swept the floors if this would have assisted progress by the group. In my experience, bright ideas never come from deliberating with pencil and paper and not too often from joint discussions. They are just as likely to arise cutting the lawns, sweeping the floors, or counting colonies—which either speaks volumes for my lack of ideas or merely indicates that scientists do differ one from another.

There are not many who are able to sit still for six to eight hours and count objects through a microscope. Fewer still who would choose to do so year after year. It does require unusual eyesight and persistence, but there is a cost. Even with the most careful adjustment of microscope and seat heights, eventually the body rebels with headaches or a stiff neck or back. These were not particularly disabling but I did have particular problems with my lumbar discs preceding the arrival of marrow colonies. As a consequence, I usually managed to be laid up in bed for a few weeks per year and eventually had two laminectomies and a spinal fusion before a normal-enough state was achieved. During these episodes, I was guilt-ridden for letting the team down but eventually managed to make up the lost time. Back problems are fairly common in those who spend a lot of time doing microscopy, and we developed considerable expertise over the years in recognizing problems early and trying to head off disability.

These are not matters that ever appear in protocols in scientific papers, but illness among research workers does occur and no account of long-term projects presents a full picture of the life involved if it fails to introduce some of the personal problems of those involved. A daily task may be performed accurately but the people involved may well be experiencing joy or despair, discomfort or worse while carrying out their tasks. We found that our students were most prone to personal problems or mood swings, particularly at times of thesis preparation or when a succession of failed experiments had occurred. At such times, the strengths of a happy team became particularly evident in many acts of kindness and support, usually well concealed. Collegiality between scientific colleagues is made much of, but far stronger is the family strength of a good team of assorted ages and lifestyles when the going gets tough for individuals. We have always been very fortunate that our technicians, mainly female, have been an admirable mixture of technical competence and human warmth. Without these key qualities, life in a busy group would be of very poor quality indeed.

SIX

The Discovery and Purification of GM-CSF

Throughout its duration, our project to purify human urinary CSF had proceeded in parallel with broader studies seeking to substantiate the view that CSF was a bona fide regulator of granulocyte and macrophage production. As part of this general information gathering, our new Ph.D. student, John Sheridan, under the guidance of Richard Stanley began a series of studies to document which murine organs contained CSF. Extracts of all 18 organs surveyed were found to contain detectable CSF. Levels of activity per milligram of protein were higher than those in serum from normal mice but not uniform. Some tissues like salivary gland or lung always contained higher levels than were present in other organ extracts. Furthermore, the CSF from these different organs did not exhibit identical characteristics when subjected to crude ammonium sulfate fractionation. These 1971 studies overlapped with those of my own in which serum CSF levels had been found to become greatly elevated within hours following an injection of bacterial flagellin or lipopolysaccharide (LPS). This very rapid response could have indicated the release of preformed CSF from the tissues to the circulation. To examine this possibility, John Sheridan made a parallel series of studies on levels of CSF in the tissues three hours after the injection of LPS. If these tissues had released their preformed CSF, their content of CSF should now be much lower. They were not. On the contrary, they were much higher, suggesting, at a minimum, that LPS had induced a rapid increase in CSF production in the tissues, apart from any associated accelerated secretion or release of CSF that may have been occurring in response to LPS. With the CSF-containing preparations from these LPS-pretreated organs it was even more evident that the properties of the CSFs were not identical from one organ to another, or in comparison with CSFs from normal organs, when analyzed by ammonium sulfate fractionation.

The possibility that there were different physical forms of CSF or different types of CSF was becoming increasingly difficult to ignore. If this conclusion was correct, then a fairly frightening prospect was that the number of potentially different CSFs might be very large indeed and that the project of purifying and characterizing CSF might be developing a nightmarish aspect in which we could become bogged down in an impossibly complex program if every organ produced different forms of CSF. This prospect was to remain with us for more than a decade and to some extent persists today in a less extreme form.

As part of his general survey work, John Sheridan extended his work on CSF extractable from tissues to CSF being produced or released from different tissues when these were incubated for two to four days in serum-free medium. The logic behind this was that if CSF was indeed present in respectable amounts in such conditioned media, it might prove a more satisfactory starting material for purification because of the lower overall protein content. Of the various organs tested, lung tissue produced much higher levels of CSF than did others. Lung tissue probably is a better source of CSF than most other tissues, although the crude culture of minced organ fragment is a far from ideal method for preserving the viability of different tissues. The loose, spongy nature of lung tissue could well have allowed a much better overall viability than for other tissues. Either way, lung-conditioned medium was regularly the most active conditioned medium, and its use in marrow cultures resulted in colony formation that was spectacularly different from the drab small macrophage colonies being stimulated by urine CSF. Colonies stimulated by crude, lung-conditioned medium were very large and were obviously a mixture of granulocytic, granulocyte-macrophage, and macrophage populations—recapitulating in a very satisfactory form the best original underlayer-stimulated cultures.

Such cultures were like a cool oasis after a long hard trek through the desert and were far too appealing to pass by. Mouse lung-conditioned medium warranted a very close analysis indeed, and experiments were undertaken to establish the best method for preparing lung-conditioned medium with the highest CSF content. Minced lung tissue seemed more effective than whole lungs in producing CSF, and lungs from mice injected three hours previously with endotoxin produced two to four times the CSF produced by normal lung tissue. A two- to fourfold difference may not seem substantial, but with the need to produce large amounts of starting material, it reduces needed mouse numbers at least twofold.

A fairly tedious procedure was standardized with pairs of technicians injecting mice intravenously then, three hours later, removing the lungs sterilely, mincing them after washing, then incubating them in capped plastic tubes containing serum-free medium. Two days later the contents of these tubes were pooled, rejecting any that had become contaminated. Batches of 800 mice were required to produce a pool of 3.2 liters of crude starting material and this became an exercise that was repeated at regular intervals for the next 10 years.

Initial analysis of the CSF present in lung-conditioned medium using a carbohydrate-splitting enzyme indicated that this CSF, like urinary CSF, was a glycoprotein. However, a remarkable difference was noted with zone sedimentation and gel filtration—procedures providing an estimate of molecular weight. Lung CSF was completely different from urine CSF in being a much smaller molecule with a molecular weight of only approximately 20,000.

For some years we referred to lung CSF as low molecular weight CSF or CSF_{MLCM}, but, because the lung CSF was clearly able to stimulate colony formation by both granulocytic and macrophage cells, we eventually adopted the terminology GM-CSF. Later analyses were to show that GM-CSF-stimulated cultures also developed eosinophil colonies, and much later, when high concentrations of GM-CSF became available, it became apparent that GM-CSF could also stimulate megakaryocyte colony formation and some erythroid colony formation. This recognition of the broader range of action did not alter the bioassay systems used for the purification of GM-CSF, which, in terms of colony numbers, were essentially monitoring granulocytic and/or macrophage colony formation.

The initial burst of progress achieved in 1972 and 1973 in characterizing the properties of low molecular weight lung CSF (GM-CSF) was about to come to a halt if not a step backward. I spent 1974 on sabbatical leave at the Swiss Institute for Cancer Research and, even though I had taken with me my own technician, further biochemical work was not able to be arranged. The time was not spent idly because, during this period, I did develop workable culture systems for growing colonies of megakaryocytes and B-lymphocytes, but I could not take GM-CSF further alone.

Furthermore, yet another change in biochemists occurred in the laboratory in Melbourne with the completion by John Sheridan of his Ph.D. and his subsequent move in 1973 to Perth as a postdoctoral fellow. As his successor in the laboratory, a biochemist postdoc, Jim Camakaris, was appointed. In my absence, conditions were not ideal for continuing work on GM-CSF. The Unit underwent a major series of staff departures in 1974, including Malcolm Moore, who moved to New York, and four postdocs. On my return, the laboratory was virtually devoid of experienced scientists and even the technicians were new and in need of training in the basic methods of bone marrow culture. Progress in purification of GM-CSF had been minimal in my absence and the situation seemed very gloomy.

Fortunately, I was about to acquire a dynamic structural protein chemist in the form of Tony Burgess as a prestigious Queen Elizabeth II Fellow. He knew nothing of the existing background regarding bone marrow colonies or CSFs, but was as eager as I to advance the GM-CSF project. He set to with vigor to recover ground that had been lost, organized the regular processing of batches of lung-conditioned medium, and began the development of a sequence of purification steps based on properties of GM-CSF that had already been established.

Our group was expected to be self-funding via its support from the Anti-Cancer Council of Victoria and later via our National Institutes of Health (NIH) grants and some smaller but always welcome grants. Financial considerations never actually prevented us from introducing

Tony Burgess at work on granulocyte-macrophage CSF.

new technical procedures that we considered might be of potential value. However, we were forced to be cautious in choosing newly developed chromatographic reagents, to reuse column materials beyond their recommended use, and to delay somewhat the acquisition of high-performance liquid chromatography (HPLC) equipment that was to prove essential for final CSF purification.

The Institute's possible lack of vision about the importance of research on hematopoietic regulators was not out of line with those of other academic organizations throughout the world. Those of us with enthusiasm had yet to produce the results justifying such enthusiasm. If we were to be seen as behaving in a rational or justifiable manner, then we were in no position to make demands for additional financial support.

Not everything Tony Burgess tried worked or produced a usable fractionation step, but momentum was maintained and by 1977 we felt confident enough to publish a six-step purification sequence achieving a 3,000-fold purification of the starting material. In this sequence we had been able to make use of the carbohydrate component of GM-CSF to allow separation using a lectin affinity column that could selectively bind carbohydrate, although not all GM-CSF bound, presaging later experiments that would document that some GM-CSF lacks carbohydrate.

Although this material met the criteria that it should produce only a single band after polyacrylamide gel electrophoresis, that this band should coincide exactly with all biological activity and that the specific activity was extremely high (1×10^7 U/mg), we had some reservations that the material might still not be able to yield an unambiguous amino acid sequence. Nevertheless we published our work to this point as the purification of GM-CSF.

In the same year, the successful purification of human urinary erythropoietin was also published in the same journal after two decades of effort. Clearly, the pace of work on the characterization and purification of hematopoietic regulators had increased abruptly. This field was now on the move and a number of laboratories were active in attempts to characterize what appeared to be the human equivalent of GM-CSF, although the data were rather ambiguous.

We had been working continuously on the culture of normal and leukemic human progenitor cells as a parallel stream of activity since 1971 and, although supplies of reasonably normal human marrow cells were at best erratic, we were as experienced as any other group in the culture and analysis of human cultures. We recognized therefore that there was no particularly good reason why we should not become involved in the characterization of human CSFs.

The practical problem, as always, was to find a reasonable source of human material with good colony-stimulating activity. Those in other laboratories working on human CSF were most often using medium from cultures of certain human neoplastic cell lines, although Abbott Laboratories in Chicago was preparing human CSF concentrates from kidney tissue cultures under contract to the National Cancer Institute to produce material for research purposes.

A survey by our group of the human cell lines we had available did not uncover any with a usable capacity to produce CSF. In his early studies, Ray Bradley had used pregnant mouse uterus as a rich source of what later became evident to be M-CSF. Such material was obvi-

Nick Nicola, Justin McCarthy, Tony Burgess, Greg Johnson, Don Metcalf, and Susie Russell in 1978.

ously not obtainable from humans but placental tissue was. Tests by one of our research assistants, Elizabeth Wilson, showed that fragments of placental tissue could produce CSF when cultured in vitro. We therefore made a decision to organize the regular daily collection of fresh human placentas from the Royal Women's Hospital and transport them to the Institute in stainless steel buckets. After cutting these placentas into roughly 1-cm cubes, the placental tissue was incubated in flasks for seven days, and the medium harvested. Activity was not wholly predictable, so each pool required a separate assay to reject inactive batches, but a feasible source material was established, if not for a major purification project, at least sufficient for some characterization work.

These studies on human placental-derived CSF by Elizabeth Wilson, Tony Burgess, and later Nick Nicola made good progress and CSF was identified that was clearly analogous to murine GM-CSF, being able to stimulate granulocytic, macrophage, and eosinophil colony formation. This CSF was further characterized by various chromatographic separation procedures and appeared to have an apparent molecular weight of 30,000—rather different from that of mouse lung GM-CSF.

The placental conditioned media studies experienced all the problems encountered earlier with human urine M-CSF and murine GM-CSF-erratic bioassays that were compounded by the highly variable nature of the human marrow cells being used in the assays. There were the usual unhelpful fractionation procedures and the ever-increasing need for more active starting material.

This was all beginning to add up to an unsatisfactory approach to producing purified human GM-CSF. With the departure of Elizabeth Wilson and the development of more promising murine CSF projects, this human project was felt to be not really feasible and the work was scaled down and eventually stopped. This was undoubtedly a sensible decision, given the indifferent supply of starting material, but was to cause us much trouble later when the issue of patent rights for GM-CSF was being disputed. In retrospect, we should probably have switched earlier in the project to work on human tumor cell line-generated material but, not having done this initially, we had gone down the track too far with placental conditioned medium to be entirely willing to backtrack and start all over again with a novel, perhaps different, CSF.

As always in these CSF projects, changes in personnel resulted in delays and slow downs in progress, and mouse lung GM-CSF was to prove no exception. It was evident to us in 1977 that our purification work would not be completed to our satisfaction until a clear amino acid sequence had been obtained. This really required preparation of much larger amounts of purified material than the microgram amounts we had so far achieved and quite possibly the addition of some further purification steps to the purification sequence. The glamour of purifying GM-CSF had come and gone with the *Journal of Biological Chemistry* publication, but the chore of producing and fractionating mouse lung-conditioned medium was continued, both to provide purified material for use in in vitro studies and to achieve the eventual goal of obtaining sequence data.

With our long-standing desire to explore the full range of biological properties of a purified CSF, much of our purified material was used in a series of in vitro studies documenting an unexpectedly broad range of functions of GM-CSF, in learning how to radiolabel the molecule without loss of biological activity, and then in tracking the fate of this radiolabeled material when injected in vivo. These were time-consuming studies but nonetheless valuable. They did, however, divert us from the production of sequence-grade GM-CSF, with the result that an astonishing six years were to elapse before sequencing was achieved. This lag would be regarded as bizarre by today's standards, but there were a number of reasons for this, not the least of which was that the technology of sequencing was still in its early phases and required relatively large amounts of purified material.

A major factor in the delayed progress of the GM-CSF project was the appointment of Tony Burgess in 1980 as the director of the newly created Ludwig Institute for Cancer Research (Melbourne Branch). By this appointment, Tony had acquired some formidable and time-consuming administrative problems—to recruit staff and develop research programs for his new institute then find laboratory space in our building and an adjacent clinical sciences building to house his embryo institute. It was great that a sister institute was being created but hardly surprising that his ability to perform and extend the biochemical purification of GM-CSF suffered. The situation was not helped by the need to house some of his new staff in our laboratories, reducing our available laboratory space. To claw back sufficient space, we were forced to convert some of our mouse rooms to rather unsatisfactory small laboratories.

In the meantime, another powerful addition to our biochemical team had arrived in the form of Nick Nicola, an experienced protein chemist and, again, a prestigious Queen Elizabeth II Fellow. Nick Nicola's major initial project in our CSF studies was to re-examine the nature of the CSFs able to be produced in culture by organs other than the lung. We now knew, or thought we knew, well enough how to recognize M-CSF and GM-CSF, but what was being produced by these other tissues? He settled on a detailed analysis of the CSF being produced by the eight most active mouse organs, and it became clear that each was able to produce biologically recognizable GM-CSF. So far so good, but a highly disturbing finding to emerge was that the GM-CSF being produced by these different organs appeared to differ dramatically in apparent molecular weight, ranging from the 23,000 of lung-derived GM-CSF to an astonishing 200,000 for muscle-derived GM-CSF. Was there some alarming artifact involved in these size estimates or was our worst nightmare being confirmed—that there might indeed be a multitude of different CSFs? We tried to keep our mounting panic within reasonable limits. We assumed, probably correctly, that different tissues might be adding highly variable amounts of carbohydrate to the GM-CSF polypeptide. There may have been a partial pathological basis for such behavior because overcrowded L-cells in culture had been found by Richard Stanley to add varying amounts of carbohydrate to M-CSF. Perhaps in the highly unfavorable organ cultures, the tissues might also be behaving erratically as viability diminished. Treatment of various organ-derived CSFs with a carbohydrate-cleaving enzyme did in fact reduce most of their apparent size heterogeneity. Why different tissues might choose to add varying amounts of carbohydrate to GM-CSF is a problem that has yet to be fully resolved. GM-CSF later acquired a reputation for exhibiting unusually prominent local actions and it was possible that a variable level of carbohydrate, if real, might have some particular role to play when GM-CSF was acting locally in widely differing tissues.

We also knew that major artifacts in size estimates could occur when gel filtration fractionation was being performed in the presence of massive amounts of unrelated proteins, a situation allowing major protein–protein interactions with the resulting anomalous behavior of proteins being monitored. Fractionation studies made using dissociating conditions and after carbohydrate removal revealed that the GM-CSFs were of much more uniform apparent size.

Nick Nicola and I did consider for a time making a major effort to mass-produce and characterize muscle-derived GM-CSF, because this form might have differed from lung-derived GM-CSF. However, this idea was dropped when events made it clear that the extra effort would be better expended in exploring what was emerging as a functionally quite different molecule, G-CSF.

There remained a problem of how to progress the GM-CSF story beyond the limping conclusion of our previous work with human urine M-CSF. Could sufficient high-quality GM-CSF be produced, despite the progressive preoccupation of Tony Burgess with his new institute? Could it be taken through to the stage of successful amino acid sequencing, both as proof of genuine purity and perhaps to allow attempts to clone the gene-encoding GM-CSF?

Tony Burgess enlisted the collaboration of Lindsay Sparrow and his colleagues at the Protein Chemistry Division of Australia's Commonwealth Scientific and Industrial Research Organisation (CSIRO), an institution with a strong reputation in protein purification and structural analysis conveniently located down the street in Parkville. The CSIRO group was interested in the project and offered to collaborate, possibly by helping mass-produce the material and certainly by fine resolution final purification. This potential expansion of our resources did not result in any immediate acceleration of progress. Indeed, we found ourselves producing the required increased amounts of starting material and, as always, performing the bioassays on any material fractionated. However, the additional fractionations performed did eventually yield material that appeared to be of exceptionally high quality and in amounts that might just suffice for sequencing.

At this stage, and because our own protein sequencing facility under Richard Simpson had yet to become operational, Tony Burgess persuaded Lee Hood and Charlie Hunkapillar at Caltech to undertake an attempted sequencing of the purified GM-CSF. A major portion of the material available was used in an initial attempt that failed to produce any sequence because of technical problems. Not to be deterred, a second batch was sent to Caltech but somehow became lost after arrival in the laboratory. With increasing frustration, yet another batch was shipped and, as a reward for persistence, this material proved not to be N-terminally blocked and yielded a sequence about which the Caltech group felt reasonably confident. With the primitive databases available in 1983, the sequence appeared to be novel and potentially usable to construct nucleotide probes with tolerable redundancy, suitable for use in an attempt to clone the GM-CSF gene.

This formally completed the purification project for GM-CSF, although Tony Burgess and Lindsay Sparrow took the analysis of lung-derived GM-CSF a little further by demonstrating the existence of two forms of this GM-CSF, an asilo form and a glycosylated form with otherwise fairly comparable apparent biological properties.

SEVEN

The Discovery and Purification of G-CSF

On several occasions when the purification of GM-CSF was in progress, I made observations suggesting the existence of what could be another distinct type of CSF. My recognition that this might be so was probably a little slow because it had not yet become routine to fix whole cultures and perform a formal analysis using stained whole-culture preparations. What had been observed was the development in some experiments of very small, dispersed colonies of only 100 to 200 cells and that these cells were small in size and might well be dying or dead. Colonies with this general appearance are common enough in cultures of poor quality, either at times of incubator failure or when CSF concentrations are barely adequate to stimulate some initial cell division, but, with progressive CSF consumption, the low CSF concentration is not sufficient to stimulate continuing proliferation, with resulting death of the aborted clones. Dying cells characteristically are of small, unconvincing size. The problem with this interpretation is that fully mature granulocytes are also of surprisingly small size and commonly look unhealthy in unstained cultures.

The previous occasions on which small, possibly dying or dead colonies were seen were those able to be explained by the use of inadequate concentrations of CSF.

Thus, in studies with Richard Shadduck of Pittsburgh, addition of his anti-M-CSF antibodies to cultures being stimulated by certain fractions of lung-conditioned medium or post-endotoxin serum led to a major reduction in the numbers of colonies developing, but there were present in some cultures a residue of small numbers of potentially dying colonies. These were merely interpreted as indicating that the added antibody had failed to neutralize all the CSF present, not that different types might have been present.

Similarly, with tail fractions from some experiments fractionating GM-CSF, sometimes such colonies were observed and again considered to be indicating no more than the presence of small concentrations of GM-CSF in fractions at the edge of the major peak.

The true explanation of what was stimulating the formation of these small, apparently dying (granulocyte) colonies was slowly to become apparent from several distinct streams of investigation.

Although mouse and human marrow cultures have some distinctive differences in the timing and pattern of colony formation, our assays in 1978 on fractionated human placental-conditioned medium using human marrow cultures were beginning to reveal, in addition to GM-CSF, a second peak of activity involving highly hydrophobic material. This latter material stimulated the formation mainly of granulocytic colonies and the cultures lacked any of the eosinophil colonies we now recognized as accompanying granulocyte-macrophage colony formation in cultures stimulated by GM-CSF, both human and murine. It seemed possible that an additional type of CSF was present in human placental-conditioned medium.

A quite separate stream of experiments had also begun to reveal evidence of a biologically active factor that was unlikely to be either GM-CSF or M-CSF. In 1969 and 1970, Ichikawa had published two highly intriguing papers involving colony formation by the murine M1 myelomonocytic cell line originally developed by Ishimoto in Kyoto. Such cells grew autonomously in vitro, unlike the behavior of primary myeloid leukemic cells. However, when Ichikawa added various types of conditioned media to the cultures, the morphology of the colonies changed dramatically from the usual compact colony composed of undifferentiated blast cells and became either fully dispersed or composed of a central tight core surrounded by a broad corona of dispers-

Catherine Dresch, Greg
Johnson, and Don Metcalf
deciding what eosinophil
colonies really look like.

ing cells. Analysis of this phenomenon showed that it was based on the
maturation of some or all of the colony cells to macrophages and less
often granulocytes. Subsequent analysis of this phenomenon by workers in Rehovot led them to propose that two distinct classes of biologically active factors were detectable in various hematopoietic cultures—
one class stimulating cell proliferation, another inducing differentiation
or maturation.

Not having access to the M1 cell line or being able to repeat the phenomenon using some of our long-established leukemic macrophage
cell lines that could generate colonies in agar, we had no particular
view on this phenomenon with leukemic colonies. We did, however,
believe that a simple distinction could not reasonably be made between
proliferation-only and differentiation-only molecules because our purified M-CSF and GM-CSF were clearly able to simulate normal hematopoietic colonies to develop by proliferation and the colony cells then
exhibited full maturation. When such studies were extended to highly
purified progenitor cells or individual developing clones, free of any

accessory cells, we felt that there was little likelihood that either CSF was acting in collaboration with some other endogenously produced differentiation factor.

Our conclusion was that both M-CSF and GM-CSF must have a dual capacity to stimulate both proliferation and maturation, unless maturation occurred automatically after a fixed number of cell divisions in the developing colony. This latter possibility had been proposed years before by workers making a kinetic analysis of the behavior of tritiated thymidine-labeled marrow populations but was no more than a speculative interpretation of the labeling data. We were not convinced by the proposal because changes in CSF concentration resulted in major size differences in developing colonies yet maturation occurred regardless of colony size and no earlier in larger than in smaller colonies—indeed, the reverse was true, although interpretation of the data was obviously complicated by the heterogeneity of colony-forming cells.

To extend this type of observation, we rechecked our available leukemic cell lines and found that, after years in culture, a leukemic cell line dating back to 1969 had undergone a major alteration in its growth characteristics in agar. When originally analyzed, this WEHI-3B cell line was growth factor dependent and the small colonies formed by this cell line might have been exhibiting some attempt at maturation. On rechecking in 1978, the cells now produced very large, tight colonies of undifferentiated cells and did not require the addition of stimulating factors to achieve cell proliferation.

When purified GM-CSF was added to cultures of these WEHI-3B cells, some Ichikawa-type maturation was observable, usually with the development around the colonies of small coronae of differentiating cells. The phenomenon reproduced, but was in no way as dramatic as, the changes described by Ichikawa with M1 cells.

What was dramatic, however, was the response of WEHI-3B cells to the addition of serum from endotoxin-injected mice. Now, precisely the same morphological changes occurred in the developing colonies as had been noted by Ichikawa. Of much more interest was the fact, noted in 1980 both by Lotem and colleagues in Rehovot and by Tony Burgess and me, that most of the colony-stimulating activity in post-endotoxin serum was separable and antigenically distinct from the active material inducing maturation in leukemic colonies. The separation used by the

Rehovot group produced three active peaks, one stimulating macrophage colonies, another granulocyte colonies, and the third having activity on M1 leukemic cells. They named their granulocyte-active material MGI-1G. With a more complete set of fractionation steps we found that the material active on leukemic cells always had the capacity to stimulate some colony formation by normal marrow cells but the colonies contained only granulocytes and, in our hands, again had the overall appearance of small dying colonies. We termed this material appearing to have two biological activities, granulocyte-macrophage differentiation factor (GM-DF) or G-CSF.

It was intriguing that the fractions of endotoxin serum stimulating the development of small mature granulocytic colonies had the same characteristic high hydrophobicity as the placental conditioned medium fractions stimulating again the exclusive formation of granulocytic colonies. The CSF involved was not likely to be M-CSF because it was not inhibited by Richard Shadduck's M-CSF antisera, and it also did not have the biological properties of GM-CSF. There did seem to be another form of CSF and presumably we had missed this on the earlier occasions when we had seen what appeared to have been small dying colonies. A report at this time by Horiuchi and Ichikawa also described the detection of what might have been a novel granulocyte colony-stimulating activity.

These various observations, when taken together, indicated strongly that we should begin a serious effort to purify G-CSF, even though in mouse cultures the factor seemed exceedingly weak in its biological activity.

We took a joint decision, when characterizing and purifying this candidate factor, to run all assays on fractionated material in parallel cultures of both normal cells and WEHI-3B leukemic cells. This introduced a complicating and potentially time-consuming element into the proposed project. However, vexations about the claimed duality of regulatory factors—proliferative versus differentiative—which we felt to be ill-based, made us resolve to have as a major goal in the project the clear-cut demonstration that a single factor could be both proliferative for normal cells and maturation-inducing for leukemic cells. In retrospect, faster progress could have been achieved had we opted for a single bioassay system with a subsequent testing of the purified material in the second type of assay. However, we wished to cover ourselves from a charge that some other active factor had been separated and lost during the sequential fractionation steps, so all fractions throughout the project were subjected to both assays.

So began the purification project on G-CSF, a project that was going to require five years for completion, and our self-inflicted slowness, because of the decision to use dual assays, arguably caused us to lose priority in some form of claim for a patent for G-CSF, with the possible loss of millions of dollars.

As always, the initial matter to be resolved was what starting material to use. We were committed to work with mouse material because of the dual needs of the two assays to be used, both involving murine cells. We regarded serum from endotoxin-injected mice as an unpromising starting material because of its high protein content.

Analysis by Nick Nicola of various mouse organ-conditioned media showed that what might be G-CSF was present in some, but that our familiar post-endotoxin lung-conditioned medium appeared to have more G-CSF activity than the others. This offered us an attractive proposition. We were already committed to mass-produce lung-conditioned medium for completion of the GM-CSF project. If the same material could also serve as source material for G-CSF, the whole laborious process could be made doubly effective with little extra effort. Careful analysis showed that an initial fractionation using differing solubility in ammonium sulfate could achieve an effective separation of most of the GM-CSF activity from the material having activity on WEHI-3B cells, and this became a routine step in generating the two types of starting material.

Nick Nicola took on the task of purifying this candidate new factor with one biochemical technician and was assisted for a year by Makoto Matsumoto, a visiting postdoctoral worker from Japan. I again took on the task of assaying all fractions in both assay systems, assisted by two biology technicians preparing the cultures. This period became a hectic time of juggling major bioassay runs, complicated by other CSF purification projects that had began to overlap from 1980 onward. All biochemical work was being undertaken in a tiny converted mouse room because of our need to house growing numbers of Ludwig Institute staff. We were, in fact, about to start a difficult project, involving a number of key issues, with probably inadequate staff numbers and certainly inadequate laboratory space. However, enthusiasm was high and our combined expertise was certainly adequate for the task ahead.

While the new protein we were about to tackle would likely have novel properties, our previous experience had given us broad guidelines about how to proceed. There was going to be need for a constant production line of lung-conditioned medium and constant processing of additional batches of material by initial separative procedures that seemed useful in eliminating contaminating protein. We now knew the necessity to avoid fractionation sequences leading to blind ends and the value of reducing overall protein loads early in the project.

Progress with the purification of this CSF proceeded slowly but surely despite continuous bioassay problems caused by the use of two assay systems. Initially, contaminating GM-CSF was present and fractionation procedures had to be chosen that were able to eliminate early on most of this material. The problem with assays using 75,000 normal marrow cells was that the new CSF could stimulate at most only 10 to 20 small colonies to develop. These were easy to miss, making scoring of unstained cultures particularly slow. Any GM-CSF present could potentially stimulate the formation of 100 to 120 larger colonies and even low concentrations of GM-CSF could therefore readily mask the small colonies stimulated by the novel CSF. On these occasions, assays on WEHI-3B cells proved more reliable because the situation was reversed in terms of the biological activity of the new CSF. However, assays using WEHI-3B cells often were unable to produce answers because of the nasty occasional tendency for WEHI-3B colonies to exhibit spontaneous differentiation.

Because many initial purification sequences ran into blind ends, resulting in the need to rearrange the sequence, we ended up producing 140 batches of lung-conditioned medium, each from 800 mice—not all of which were carried through to full purification.

Progress was again slowed by my absence for a year in Holland and at Cambridge University. During this period, Greg Johnson stood in for me with the bioassays but the project had run into serious problems.

In this purification project, we had included separation by high-performance liquid chromatography (HPLC)—then a fairly new procedure for separative protein chemistry—but its use resulted in a dramatic rise in the purification achieved from 100-fold up to 400,000-fold. Having reached what seemed likely to be a potentially final purification stage, the project ran into a disastrous phase where the highly purified material repeatedly vanished, with loss of weeks of preceding work. Was this loss due to degradation or adsorption? Either was possible, but, by trial and error using various detergents, we established that the losses seemed to be due to the unusually sticky nature of the molecule and its loss by adsorption to glassware and plastic surfaces. Working through this period of frustration occupied many months, and it was not until 1982 that purified G-CSF was obtained. This material reproducibly stimulated the formation by mouse bone marrow cells only of small granulocytic colonies but was highly active in enforcing differentiation in WEHI-3B colonies. At every stage, the two bioassays generated bioactivity peaks with identical locations and our conclusion was that the two responses were being induced by the same molecule.

Nick Nicola was of the view that our first and only publication on the purification of this molecule should give it the name of differentiation factor, a name that had been introduced originally by the Japanese workers. I was equally obstinate that we had accept it for what it was, in terms of its action on normal cells—a granulocyte colony-stimulating factor. We both had our way and the title of the paper, "Purification of a Factor Inducing Differentiation in Murine Myelo-monocytic Leukemia Cells: Identification as Granulocyte Colony-Stimulating Factor," reflected our twin objectives—purifying the new CSF and establishing that a proliferative regulator could also be a differentiation-inducing factor. Thereafter, the molecule was referred to simply as G-CSF.

Our Israeli competitors had demonstrated that in suspension cultures of bone marrow cells with material of this type no increase in cell numbers occurred, simply the progressive appearance of mature granulocytes. This was the basis for their view that a factor of this type was merely inducing differentiation or maturation. However, the clonal cultures provided the true explanation for the type of result they obtained. Only 20 in 75,000 marrow cells respond by sustained clonal proliferation to stimulation by G-CSF. If each generates a colony of 250 cells in seven days then the 20 cells would generate only 5,000 maturing cells, with the remainder of the cells originally added to the culture dying during this period. Thus no rise in cell numbers would be observable, merely an increase in the proportion of mature granulocytes present, with a fall in total cell numbers. The phenomenon documented the superiority of clonal cultures over "black box" suspension cultures for revealing the events actually occurring during culture.

Having painfully accumulated enough purified material, part was sent to our newly established sequencing laboratory where Richard Simpson performed a meticulous job in obtaining maximal possible sequence data. He ended up by successfully obtaining sequence data from over 60 percent of the molecule—far more than would have been needed to generate adequate nucleotide probes for sequencing.

Our progress in producing and sequencing G-CSF was slow because it was one of the earliest projects of our new sequencing laboratory. Even so, considerable sequence data were available by June or July of 1984 and a provisional patent application could have been filed with the purification, properties, and partial amino acid sequence. As things turned out, human and murine G-CSF are very similar and this application would have been enabling for the subsequent cloning of cDNAs both for murine and human G-CSF.

At that time it was a little unclear whether patent applications needed to be based on cloning data or could merely be based on amino acid sequence data. We were no doubt naïve in our relative lack of awareness of the importance of filing patent applications but no one yet had grounds for believing that agents like G-CSF would prove to be worth billions of dollars. No one had ever shown CSFs to be active in vivo and, on the face of it, the weakly active G-CSF seemed a rather poor candidate for what seemed to us an expensive exercise of filing a provisional patent application. How times and practices were to change in the following 17 years!

In the event, we did not file a provisional patent application until October 30, 1985, and, in the meantime, Chugai (Tokyo) had filed a patent application based on amino acid sequence data for human G-CSF on July 25, 1984.

It is somewhat irrelevant that our patent attorney advised in October 1985 and again in October 1986 that our patent application was not worth pursuing, in part because it was based only on a partial amino acid sequence. Patent applications based on cDNA clones had by then already been filed by Amgen (Thousand Oaks, CA [August 1985] and by Chugai [September 1985]). The attorney's comment regarding the doubtful value of an amino acid sequence alone was actually correct advice as patent practice was understood in 1985. It has only been the subsequent increasing ease and predictability of cloning based on sequence data that now would allow amino acid sequence data to be more obviously enabling and therefore to constitute a strong provisional patent application.

The fatal error we made was in not filing a provisional patent application on one of the days when our amino acid sequence data were obtained (June 14, 1984, or at worst July 6, 1984). In view of subsequent events, such a patent application might well have led to a substantial financial buyout of the patent by one of the companies concerned with the development of human G-CSF.

There had been a temporary loss of momentum in our purification work on G-CSF after the submission of the manuscript describing its purification, and this also contributed to our slowness in collecting sequence data. This phenomenon had also occurred in the GM-CSF project. The origin of this curious pattern is in part psychological. After one spends years of effort to achieve purification there is an inevitable feeling of let down when success has been achieved. The G-CSF story warns of the consequences of losing momentum when initial scientific success has been achieved.

Part of the purified G-CSF generated in 1982–1983 was used to establish the nature of the actions of G-CSF on marrow cultures and to document that G-CSF could in fact *initiate* the proliferation of a much wider range of granulocyte-macrophage progenitor cells but could only sustain the proliferation of a small subset of these. G-CSF was also successfully radiolabeled to establish by autoradiography the range of marrow cell types expressing receptors for G-CSF. These were blast cells, granulocytic cells, and monocytic cells. It was also documented that while WEHI-3B cells expressed receptors for G-CSF, an unresponsive subline—WEHI-3B D⁻—lacked detectable G-CSF receptors.

To verify that the hydrophobic fractions from human placental-conditioned medium did represent human G-CSF, we had documented that the candidate human G-CSF could cross-compete for the binding of ^{125}I-labeled murine G-CSF to mouse bone marrow cells, indicating not only that this human CSF was indeed G-CSF but had to be of closely similar structure to permit the cross-reactivity, unlike the situation with human and murine GM-CSF.

Our short two-year period as the sole possessors of purified G-CSF was about to become abruptly terminated in 1984. Two groups, Nagata and colleagues in Tokyo and a consortium of workers at the Sloan-Kettering Institute in New York and Amgen in California, had been working hard on the purification of human G-CSF. Success in purifying human G-CSF by both groups was to be followed immediately by cloning of cDNAs for G-CSF and the mass production of recombinant G-CSF.

Our work had led to the discovery and characterization of the actions of G-CSF as detectable in conventional agar cultures. A picture had emerged that G-CSF was a quite selective proliferative agent for a subset of granulocyte precursors and, through collaborative studies with Mathew Vadas and Angel Lopez, that G-CSF was able to activate the functional actions of mature neutrophils. It had become established as a third distinct CSF, but recognition of its full potential would need to await its first use in vivo.

EIGHT

The Discovery and Purification of Multi-CSF (IL-3)

In 1968, Noel Warner's group in our Unit had been inducing the development of a large series of primary murine tumors, mostly plasmacytomas, by the injection of mineral oil or pristane into responsive BALB/c mice. One of these primary animals (WEHI-3) appeared highly unusual in that the enlarged lymph nodes were greenish in color. Analysis showed that this tumor was in fact a rare myelomonocytic leukemia and transplantation studies led to the derivation of four very different sublines of transplantable tumors (WEHI-3A–D), one (WEHI-3D) being remarkable in being tetraploid and in generating tetraploid mature neutrophil progeny. WEHI-3B was of more interest to Malcolm Moore and me because it was capable of forming small, if rather unhealthy, colonies in agar culture, particularly when stimulated by CSF-containing material. WEHI-3B leukemic cells were later established by Chris Wyss in our laboratory as a continuously growing cell line. At some stage in this process the line altered its in vitro growth characteristics to become the autonomous cell line able to form large colonies in agar—the cell line used by us to monitor the purification of G-CSF.

With cultures of the original WEHI-3B tumor cells in 1968, I had observed a curious phenomenon in which coculture of the tumor cells with normal marrow cells led to colony formation demonstrable as originating from the cultured normal cells. This phenomenon was remarkable for two reasons. We had never observed before that coculture of tumor cells with normal cells could result in the stimulation of colony formation by normal cells, suggesting that this cell line had an unusual capacity to produce CSF. More remarkable was the curious appearance of the small numbers of colonies developing. These were composed of uniformly dispersed cells in globular clouds. I had never before observed colonies with this peculiar morphology and pointed out in the published description of these studies that a novel CSF and/or cell type must be involved. On occasion, Malcolm and I had also observed the development of small clusters of giant cells with what could have been multiple or multilobed nuclei. They could have been megakaryocytes, but we hesitated to reach this conclusion because no specific stain for megakaryocytes was then available (now acetyl-cholinesterase would be used for this purpose) and because aging macrophages in colonies can undergo cell fusion with the formation of large multinucleate cells.

These observations had been set aside as curiosities for possible further exploration at some future date. In retrospect, they represented the first detection of Multi-CSF (IL-3), because at very low concentrations this agent is quite distinctive in stimulating the formation by marrow cells of small numbers of dispersed colonies whose cells still remain only partially characterized.

A quite separate stream of studies was begun in our laboratories in 1973 by an American sabbatical leave worker, John Parker, who had a background of working with lectin-stimulated proliferation of T lymphocytes. Tom McNeill, another postdoc who had been in our laboratory in 1968, had recently observed that the lectin phytohemagglutin seemed able to induce spleen cells to produce CSF. In simultaneous studies, John Parker continued this general line of enquiry by investigating in more detail whether lectins of this type could provoke T lymphocytes to produce CSF. Lectins proved able to stimulate spleen and lymph node populations to produce CSF and he established that it was indeed T lymphocytes in the mitogen-stimulated spleen cell populations that were the source of the CSF. He settled on pokeweed mitogen as the most effective lectin to use for spleen cell activation and, of the various mouse strains tested, BALB/c spleen cells seemed to be the most active and reliable. Apart from being a novel source of highly active CSF-containing conditioned medium, pokeweed mitogen-stimulated spleen-conditioned medium (SCM) proved able to stimulate the formation of the same curious dispersed colonies as had developed in the earlier cocultures of marrow cells with WEHI-3B cells. We wrote a paper describing these dispersed colonies in which the referees forced me to change the name of the colonies to eosinophil-like colonies. We did have some Giemsa-stained cell preparations from these colonies in which cells were present that could have been eosinophils, but I was certainly not happy to refer to them as eosinophil colonies. This assignation of the name "eosinophil" to these dispersed colonies was quite wrong. They are certainly not composed of eosinophils and later work with an eosinophil-specific stain (Luxol Fast Blue) made it clear that while SCM does in fact stimulate eosinophil as well as granulocyte and macrophage colonies to develop, mouse eosinophil colonies have a very different gross morphology, usually looking like small granulocytic colonies.

SCM was to prove to have some remarkable properties. In 1974, while working for a year in Lausanne, I used SCM as reliable material for stimulating the formation of colonies that we showed were composed of megakaryocytes. To SCM therefore goes the credit of providing the first stimulating material for growing megakaryocyte colonies. In 1976, Greg Johnson and I discovered its ability to stimulate multipotential and erythroid colony formation in cultures of mouse fetal liver cells in the absence of added erythropoietin. No doubt small amounts of erythropoietin may have been present in the human plasma used in the cultures, but it was certainly a novelty to be able to grow large red erythroid colonies without the addition of erythropoietin. Furthermore, the multipotential colonies were an astonishing addition to the hematopoietic colony types now able to be grown in vitro because they could contain cells of at least five lineages.

These developments had been proceeding at a time when the major projects in the laboratory were the purification of lung GM-CSF and the imminent commencement of attempts to purify G-CSF. Although our group now contained 10 scientists and students, it was not large enough to contemplate with equanimity the additional task of purifying what could have been several novel lineage-specific colony-stimulating factors in SCM.

We had formed the view that material like SCM was likely to contain multiple regulatory factors. These potentially might include one that was specific for megakaryocytes, one for multipotential cells, one for eosinophils, and one for erythroid cells. Tests on WEHI-3B-conditioned medium revealed that it had a comparable range of biological actions to SCM, but with one consistent difference—it seemed relatively inefficient in stimulating erythroid colony formation or at least the formation of bright red, fully hemoglobinized erythroid colonies. Was the leukemia-derived material different from that being produced by mitogen-activated normal T-lymphocytes? This seemed a valid enough speculation at the time.

As usual, we slipped gradually into an ever more demanding project to examine what factors might be in SCM or WEHI-3B conditioned medium. At first, this embryonic project was assigned to a research assistant under the guidance of Tony Burgess, then later to a new Ph.D. student, Rob Cutler, under the supervision of Nick Nicola. Greg Johnson and I shared the various marrow and fetal liver assays required.

Because we were convinced that multiple regulatory factors must be responsible, including almost certainly GM-CSF, our initial efforts were not really undertaken with purification as the goal but to provide evidence for the existence of potentially separable lineage-specific molecules.

Other workers, including Mike Dexter and his group in Manchester and Malcolm Moore and his group in New York, held an opposite view that material like SCM and WEHI-3B-conditioned medium might well contain a novel multipotential factor. If so, this was the Holy Grail of hematopoietic regulators, likely not only to be multipotential, but possibly also to be able to stimulate the proliferation and expansion of stem cell populations. The possibilities for clinical exploitation of such a molecule in marrow transplantation had much appeal for these groups.

As is often the case with controversies, both views turned out to have some validity. SCM does contain a multiplicity of hematopoietic regu-

Frank Lee, Mike Dexter, Don Metcalf, and Nick Nicola at a CIBA
Symposium in London.

lators, but it also contains one multipotential regulator that met many
of the expectations of those agreeing with the Manchester/New York
view. For example, I found that mouse SCM had a truly extraordinary
action in cultures of human marrow cells, in stimulating the exclusive
formation of eosinophil colonies. This remains the most dramatic
example yet encountered of selective colony formation by unfractionated bone marrow cells. We carried out a few biochemical experiments
to establish the general properties of the active molecule responsible
for stimulating human eosinophil colony formation but took this story
no further after publication of these findings.

What had been discovered was later to become known as inter-
leukin-5 (IL-5), and the murine version of IL-5 happens to be fully active on human cells, in contrast to most murine regulators, which have
no action on human cells. In the now large literature on IL-5, the initial
publication is rarely referred to. By the tough rules in this field, credit
is reserved for those making definitive advances like purification or
cloning of a regulator. It is not sufficient to discover and partially characterize a molecule. In retrospect, we regret letting this discovery pass

undeveloped, but we were attempting to cope with several major projects simultaneously and were about to enter an even more demanding project. We felt that we did not have sufficient available resources and something had to be dropped. At least, I was left with the joy of having seen and worked with some truly remarkable cultures and retain a fond private regard for IL-5 as a briefly loved but abandoned stepchild.

We now know that SCM also contains GM-CSF, IL-6, stem cell factor, leukemia inhibitory factor (LIF), Flk ligand, IL-9, and doubtless other as yet unidentified regulators. Activated T lymphocytes are a remarkable source of such regulatory factors. Our presumption that multiple factors were present was in fact correct, but it was not to prove very helpful in the particular project we were about to attempt.

Our view that multiple factors were present in SCM progressively led us into a very inefficient program requiring separate bioassays on fetal liver and adult marrow cells, each of a highly demanding nature because all colonies needed exact morphological identification. The assay cultures often needed repetition because colony formation of the highest quality was required. We were seeking evidence from one type of fractionation or another that some segregation of colony-stimulating activity was achievable and, with concentration-dependent changes in the types of colony being stimulated, such evidence as was obtained was difficult to reproduce and rather unconvincing.

The production of highly active batches of SCM was very variable and all 2-l batches prepared had to be separately assayed to exclude ones with inferior activity. The fetal liver assays required the use of preselected heat-inactivated human plasma to allow the formation of good erythroid colonies. This necessitated pretesting large numbers of human plasma batches to select ones with a satisfactory capacity to support the formation of such colonies. There were times when pretesting of SCM and plasma batches so dominated the working day that assays on fractionated material often were delayed.

To make matters worse, our predilection for things leukemic and the apparent differences between SCM and WEHI-3B-conditioned medium led us into an even more foolish decision, to fractionate both starting materials in parallel, so doubling the problems and workloads.

If progress was being made in this cumbersome non-project, it was only apparent in our most optimistic moments during the period 1978–

1980. We had uncovered no evidence making our multiple factor hypothesis untenable, so the work continued in the hope of picking up some novel lineage-specific factor. For me at least, the hope of acquiring new lineage-specific factors was particularly appealing. There were a number of basic questions that might be resolvable concerning the possible ability of regulatory factors to enforce differentiation commitment in bipotential or multipotential cells and lineage-specific factors ought to be powerful reagents in such studies. The alternative, that there was a single multipotential factor, of course also had its attractions, although I had no particular desire to become involved in stem cell biology if this was going to require in part a return to in vivo experiments.

There then occurred a curious episode in which a second group in the Institute under John Schrader became involved in what seemed potentially to be a duplicative program to ours—a fractionation analysis of mitogen-stimulated spleen cell–conditioned medium. Granted the mitogen used was concanavalin-A, not pokeweed mitogen, but the two conditioned media seemed closely similar. John Schrader had established that his conditioned medium led to the emergence of long-term culturable, factor-dependent cells from bone marrow termed by him "persisting cells," or P cells. These were later proved to be mast cells. His assays on fractionated conditioned medium were therefore more highly focused, with the use of a single assay, and his progress with his project to purify the active factor was no doubt assisted by assessing the value of some of our fractionation procedures. His group was certainly faster in achieving what was clearly highly purified material.

I must say that there were times when it was irritating for two groups to be rather overtly in competition and do not recommend this as a method for ensuring more rapid overall success for the institute involved. Competition between distant groups is the usual situation, not between groups on adjacent floors. Our resources were already stretched thin and we could not accelerate our own cumbersome program, but, until the nature of the active factors in such media was resolved, it was not clear whether the two programs were in fact in conflict or were merely proceeding in parallel streams.

Other groups were also active on this subject, with the Manchester group under Mike Dexter publishing preliminary data suggesting that only a single multipotential factor was responsible for many of the types of biological effects being monitored. In collaborative experiments, I produced some of the data for this study, but disagreeing with the conclusions reached, I chose not to be an author on the paper. Malcolm Moore's group, working with human material, obtained a highly enriched CSF that they believed might be the human equivalent of the murine molecule, and termed it pluripoietin. This molecule later turned out to be G-CSF.

Unknown to any of these groups, one group under Jim Ihle at Memphis was about to drop a bombshell. This group had been working with spleen cells from mice lacking T lymphocytes. Monitoring of the enzyme 20α hydroxysteroid dehydrogenase in these cells indicated that a sharp rise in the levels of this enzyme was inducible by a factor in activated T lymphocyte-conditioned medium or WEHI-3B-conditioned medium. This biochemical activity was found to correlate with an ability to stimulate the proliferation of the factor-dependent cell line, FDC-P1, developed in Mike Dexter's laboratory in Manchester. Using WEHI-3B-conditioned medium as starting material and the rapid FDC-P1 bioassay, the group very quickly succeeded in purifying the active factor to homogeneity as a protein of 28,000 molecular weight, and under the name interleukin-3.

When this study was published in 1982 much disquiet arose in hematologists that this might be the factor, or one of the factors, being sought in other laboratories. Through a series of collaborations with various laboratories, including that of John Schrader, IL-3 was shown by 1983 to indeed be a multipotential hematopoietic regulatory factor able to stimulate granulocyte, macrophage, eosinophil, megakaryocyte, multipotential, erythroid, and mast cell proliferation. Our later tests on purified IL-3 showed that, at very low concentrations, it stimulated the curiously dispersed colonies I had first noted in 1968 as being stimulated by WEHI-3B cells when cocultured with normal marrow cells. Quite clearly, a new CSF had been added to the repertoire of characterized factors.

For some time we had been referring to this emerging factor as multipotential CSF or Multi-CSF to maintain some uniformity in our nomenclature and, being stubborn, I often continue to refer to IL-3 as Multi-CSF, unless the recombinant product of the cloned IL-3 gene is being referred to. This is illogical behavior, granted, but I felt that having first noted and described the curious IL-3-stimulated dispersed colonies 14 years earlier, I had some proprietary rights. It has turned out that the GM-CSF gene and the IL-3 (Multi-CSF) gene are adjacent and are almost certainly related evolutionarily; furthermore, their receptors also share a common β-chain. To this degree, therefore, I still believe that the molecule has a proper claim to be a CSF, so my obstinate behavior persists and is usually tolerated with good enough humor by my colleagues.

By 1983, all basic aspects of the function of IL-3 (Multi-CSF) had been established. We could have ceased work on our project, but it was the basis of Rob Cutler's Ph.D. thesis and we felt it proper to allow him to complete the purification of Multi-CSF from SCM. Our purification was not completed and published until 1985, by then merely as a formal record that the project had been completed and that the normal cell-derived factor was apparently identical to that produced by WEHI-3B cells.

As we had done with the earlier purified CSFs, we radiolabeled Multi-CSF and, by autoradiography, established the range of marrow cells expressing receptors for this regulator. We also analyzed the fate of ^{125}I-labeled Multi-CSF when injected into mice.

Before closing this Multi-CSF chapter, it is of interest to comment on the peculiar features of the WEHI-3B leukemic cell line that figured so prominently in the evolution of this story. The actual WEHI-3B line used as a source material by a number of groups attempting the purification of IL-3 was a derivative line appearing in Malcolm Moore's laboratory in New York. It is known as WEHI-3B D$^-$ because, as discussed earlier, it is refractory to differentiation induction by G-CSF, failing to express membrane receptors for G-CSF. How it evolved from the original WEHI-3B D$^+$ cells is unclear because it is a near-tetraploid cell line. It is often regarded as the only WEHI-3B cell line producing IL-3, but this is not so because WEHI-3B D$^+$ cells also produce IL-3, although in lesser amounts. From our 1968 experiments, and knowing now the peculiar characteristics of colonies stimulated by very low concentrations of IL-3, it is clear that from the outset WEHI-3B cells produced IL-3. It has subsequently been shown that this autocrine production in WEHI-3B cells is based on constitutive activation of the IL-3 gene by insertion of an intracisternal-A particle upstream of the gene.

No stimulation of normal colony formation was ever observed in cocultures of marrow cells with the other original WEHI-3 sublines A, C, or D, although these did not proliferate in culture, so it remains unclear whether the activating insertion was present in the original WEHI-3 tumor. The WEHI-3 leukemia is commonly cited as an example of autocrine growth factor production leading to neoplastic transformation. However, this is quite speculative because the original cells were not capable of exhibiting autonomous growth in vitro and, as might have been expected in such a situation, although as shall be discussed later, this rule for autocrine growth factor-producing cells is not invariably true.

With all these uncertainties, it is nonetheless astonishing how Noel Warner's odd myelomonocytic leukemia came to play such a dominant role in the story of hematopoietic regulators, being used to monitor the purification of G-CSF, as a source for IL-3 (Multi-CSF) and later as a useful cell in which to transfect receptors for all manner of hematopoietic regulators to map substructural regions in these receptors. It has earned a remarkable place in the history of hematopoiesis. It is in fact quite interesting how many major discoveries are attributable to the use of a handful of leukemic cell lines—M1 for IL-6, LIF, and oncostatin M (OSM); HL60, murine erythroleukemia (MEL), and U937 for many studies on maturation induction. Other newer leukemic lines like M7 are beginning to generate an equally honorable track record.

NINE

The End of the Beginning: An Appraisal of Progress So Far

With the resolution of the multipotential regulator controversy and inclusion of interleukin-3 (IL-3, or Multi-CSF) into the gang of four CSFs able to regulate granulocyte-macrophage production, the discovery and purification phases for the murine colony-stimulating factors ended.

Beginning with the striking phenomenon of granulocyte-macrophage colony formation by mouse bone marrow cells when stimulated by organ fragments or medium conditioned by various tissues, we had convinced ourselves that the phenomenon was due to stimulation by a glycoprotein produced by various organs and that this glycoprotein, termed colony-stimulating factor, was detectable in the serum and urine with its concentration varying in situations involving perturbations of granulocyte-macrophage populations.

We had come to recognize that granulocyte-macrophage colony formation was a more complex phenomenon than at first seemed apparent, and, with the later development of similar culture techniques for eosinophil, megakaryocyte, erythroid, and multipotential colony formation, a rather complete analytical system had emerged for analyzing in detail the biology of hematopoietic populations.

Techniques for growing various erythroid colonies had been developed in Toronto, beginning in 1961, by Stephenson, Axelrad, Tepperman, and colleagues. These systems were clearly allowing the detection and characterization of erythropoietin, the regulator of more mature erythroid precursors, but this was not a subject of central interest to us. It was best left to our Canadian and U.S. colleagues.

We had concentrated on the granulocyte-macrophage colony-forming system, later recognizing from work of Paul Chervenick that eosinophil colonies also developed in such cultures.

While we often found ourselves culturing human marrow-derived colonies, we had tended to focus our efforts on murine cultures and their stimulation by CSF. Even though our first efforts to purify CSF had involved human urine, for a long period after this we concentrated on murine CSFs. We then progressively had recognized that more than one CSF existed, turning our efforts in sequence from M-CSF to GM-CSF then G-CSF and finally Multi-CSF (IL-3).

Throughout this 15-year period we had few competitors who were making sustained contributions to the purification and characterization of these murine CSFs. As a consequence, through Richard Stanley, first in Melbourne then in Toronto and New York, M-CSF had been purified and its actions established. We had purified and characterized GM-CSF and G-CSF while the efforts of several groups to characterize murine Multi-CSF had been abruptly truncated by the work of Jim Ihle and his co-workers in purifying IL-3 (Multi-CSF).

Our own view was that these four CSFs represented a group of functionally related regulators corresponding for the granulocyte-macrophage lineages to the single regulator, erythropoietin, for erythropoiesis. We had few firm grounds for confidence in portraying these four CSFs as *the* regulatory system for granulocyte and macrophage populations. We had buried under the carpet some worrying observations that there might well be differing forms of GM-CSF and that not all M-CSFs seemed to have identical properties. G-CSF and Multi-CSF seemed less of a worry in this regard.

Why did we believe that the CSFs were a functionally related family? The major reason, I suppose, was that they stimulated somewhat similar, if individually distinct, granulocyte-macrophage colony formation by bone marrow cells, the defining property for the name CSF. But was this simply a self-fulfilling terminology? The molecules were of quite different sizes when glycosylated and the small amounts of amino acid sequence data obtained indicated no obvious homology between the four. However, the four CSFs were beginning to reveal a common pattern of polyfunctionality, to be discussed shortly, which tended to unify them. Moreover, various tissues seemed able to simultaneously produce at least three of these CSFs and in response to comparable inducing signals. The odd man out in the group was Multi-CSF, readily able to be produced by lymphocytes in vitro but not detectable in vivo in normal mice. Also of likely relevance in unifying these CSFs were observations made by Nick Nicola and Francesca Walker that binding of one CSF to membrane receptors had predictable consequences for the ability of the cells to bind other CSFs, suggesting some sort of close functional interaction between these four regulators.

Having said all this, it must be admitted that it was somewhat presumptuous to give these four regulators the common name of CSF, implying that they were in fact a tight family of regulators. It was not until considerably later when the CSF genes and their receptors had been cloned that more cogent reasons emerged for associating at least two of these CSFs—GM-CSF and Multi-CSF—into a paired group. It certainly helped us in the early 1980s to talk and write about the CSFs as a functional family and was a quite defensible simplification to allow the regulatory biology of granulocyte-macrophage populations to be introduced to general audiences. It was however not much more than a stratagem for erecting some signposts in what had previously been uncharted territory.

I do not recall that we spent much time formally considering the possibility that there would be four matching human CSFs for the four murine CSFs. Despite this lack of clear formulation, we obviously must have had such a working understanding. We had, after all, begun with human M-CSF, which, although having some odd functional deficiencies, was obviously related to murine M-CSF. When we were working with human placental-derived CSFs we had no hesitation in identifying human analogues for GM-CSF and G-CSF. We had not encountered a human molecule corresponding to Multi-CSF at that time nor had any other group produced evidence for such a molecule, so this CSF remained somewhat in limbo.

In the later stages of our work on the murine CSFs, other groups had begun characterizing human CSFs, mainly being produced by tumor cell lines. Not having access to these particular cell lines, we fairly wisely had not been tempted to extend still further our range of activities but nonetheless followed these developments with proprietary interest. The initial results from these groups were fairly messy, given by then the quite detailed information available on how to purify murine CSFs and the stringent requirements to be met before purification could be achieved.

Ultimately, the group achieving success with the purification of human GM-CSF was that of Judy Gasson and David Golde at UCLA using the Mo leukemia cell line. In parallel, the two groups achieving success finally with the purification of G-CSF were those of Shige Nagata and colleagues in Tokyo and of Karl Welte, Erich Platzer, and Malcolm Moore in New York when finally the material was passed to Larry Souza's group at Amgen. These successes can be dated approximately to 1985–1986, sometime after completion of purification of the murine CSFs. I remain uncertain whether anyone actually ever purified human Multi-CSF from native sources.

From their biological actions, the four human CSFs did match well the four murine CSFs, which reinforced the conclusion that murine and human hematopoiesis were closely similar processes, but of course did nothing to further substantiate the assumption that these four CSFs were a closely integrated family of regulators.

The discovery and popularization of the four CSFs, together with parallel work on erythropoietin, had begun to attract many workers to this field and these regulators had begun to be regarded as prototypes for possible additional regulators that might be awaiting discovery. Was our group fully aware that other regulators lay awaiting discovery? The answer is that we were indeed, although discovery at this stage seemed to require an available bioassay system offering reasons for suspecting the presence of some novel active agent.

At this time, most work on the regulation of T and B lymphocytes tended to be divorced from the growing knowledge of hematopoietic regulators. Immunologists had built up a massive folklore that lymphocytes were different from other cells and that lymphocytes were largely regulated by antigens of exquisite specificity, not by mundane regulatory factors. The exquisite selectivity of antigen stimulation was beyond dispute and did indeed seem a more sophisticated system than the situation with granulocyte-macrophage populations, where most cells seemed to respond to a single regulatory protein. Working within an immunology institute made us very aware of the self-awarded superiority of cellular immunologists, who regarded granulocyte-macrophage populations as a very low order of life—mere garbage removers. That our granulocyte-macrophage culture systems had in fact become better characterized and more sophisticated than available T or B lymphocyte cultures seems to have escaped notice by those who comforted themselves with such exoticisms as tolerance, memory, etc.

What struck us about lymphoid populations and their biology was the relative crudeness of the antigen-based control systems. Massive numbers of receptors were present on lymphocytes and high concentrations of antigen were required to elicit these selective proliferative responses. To us this did not seem a particularly sophisticated regulatory system. We assumed that lymphocytes, like other hematopoietic populations, would be controlled, at least in part, by regulatory molecules that were as efficient as erythropoietin or the CSFs. We felt that most immunologists seemed to be exhibiting ostrich-like behavior in failing to take note of the lessons emerging from the other hematopoietic populations.

There were two notable exceptions to this otherwise fairly dismal record. I say "dismal" because there were in fact far larger numbers of cellular immunologists than experimental hematologists but most were busy amusing themselves with evocative word-spinning based often on cell biology of barely modest quality. The two exceptions were those who had purified IL-1 in 1981 as an agent able to initiate the activation of T lymphocytes and the groups purifying IL-2 in 1978 as a selective proliferative stimulus for T lymphocytes. In neither case were clonal culture systems developed, so neither advance allowed the hierarchical populations of T lymphocytes to be defined or characterized. Nevertheless, these two regulators were to be important precursors for immunologists in their delayed search for regulators controlling T- and B-lymphoid populations.

We watched with much interest from the sidelines these developments with IL-1 and IL-2 but certainly had no intention of becoming enmeshed in the continuing circus of cellular immunology. IL-1 did arguably seem to have some enhancing effects on the ability of M-CSF to stimulate early granulocyte and macrophage precursors, but IL-2 had no obvious actions on granulocyte-macrophage populations.

As noted earlier, we had already had in our hands IL-5 and dropped the regulator to concentrate on G-CSF and Multi-CSF. We had also, with some misgivings, decided not to pursue the possible existence of variants of GM-CSF or M-CSF. So we were well aware that other regulators might well be awaiting discovery. As it turned out, we took no part in the later discovery of additional hematopoietic regulators active on granulocyte-macrophage populations of which three—stem cell factor, IL-6, and Flk-ligand—stood out as having significant proliferative actions on granulocyte and/or macrophage populations. Of the known hematopoietic regulators, now totaling about 25, these latter three remain the only significant agents acting on committed granulocyte-macrophage progenitor cells in addition to the four CSFs. Analysis has shown that these three regulators have a much weaker action than that of the CSFs in terms of the concentration required to elicit detectable responses in vitro, so the original proposal that the CSFs were of particular importance as regulators of granulocyte and macrophage populations still remains correct today.

When it was possible to work with agents active on the generation by stem cells of various progenitor cells, agents like SCF and Flk-ligand would become recognized as interacting with the CSFs to stimulate this process to indirectly enhance the formation of granulocytes and macrophages. These more complex developments were still almost a decade in the future.

Although it was not realized at the time, 1983 was the end of an era, and very little would remain the same after this time. New entrants to the field were about to propel us into the world of billion-dollar products, recombinant materials were to become available to all, and there was to be the discovery of a sizable number of novel candidate hematopoietic regulators for the majority of which there was no background biological information. Not only would the pace of work accelerate but the manner of making discoveries would become permanently altered.

The period from 1965 to 1983 can be characterized as one in which reductionist biology had been applied to the confusion of cells under-

going hematopoiesis in the bone marrow. Could the immature populations be stratified into some probable sequence? What were the rela-
tionships between the different hematopoietic lineages? Were lineage
commitment and cellular hierarchies irreversible? What was the general nature of the regulators able to influence various types of hematopoiesis? What functions could be attributed to these regulators?
Where were they produced and in response to what induction signals?
Was there evidence that the regulators acted directly on responding
cells and could more than one regulator act simultaneously on individual cells?

Resolution of these questions needed a number of major technical
advances. High-efficiency cultures had been developed in which the
progeny of individual precursor cells in most lineages could be enu-
merated and analyzed. Methods had been developed for obtaining in
pure form the various types of hematopoietic precursor cells. Candidate
regulators had been produced in pure form in very small amounts but
sufficient for use in analyzing their actions on purified target cells.
Although further advances of course were to continue after 1983,
progress until this time had been very good indeed.

In cellular terms, one type of multipotential self-renewing
"stem" cell had been characterized using the spleen colony technique
and was shown to be able to generate both committed progenitor
cells as well as maturing progeny. Such spleen colony-forming
cells from the rat had been purified by Irv Goldschneider in our group
using fluorescence-activated cell sorting and was shown to have
the morphology of small mononuclear (lymphocyte-like) cells, most
of which were not in active cell cycle. Their committed progenitor
cell progeny in the murine system had similarly been purified by
Nick Nicola using fluorescence-activated cell sorting and identified
as somewhat larger mononuclear cells, usually with the morphology of blast cells, and this population had been shown to be mainly
in cell cycle. Fluorescence-activated cell sorting had not been able to
segregate progenitor cells into distinct subsets of cells committed
to one or the other lineage, so contrary views continued to be expressed
whether or not lineage commitment only occurred after significant con-
tact with a relevant regulator. Most culture studies had indicated that
lineage switching was not possible by committed progenitor cells

nor could progenitor cells dedifferentiate to spleen colony-forming "stem" cells.

No in vitro culture system had been developed for spleen colony-forming cells, so the manner by which they generated progenitor cells remained unknown. However, reliable methods had been developed for clonally culturing cells in all the major cell lineages, with reservations only about the methods used for the clonal culture of T lymphocytes. In vitro colonies in conventional cultures had been shown to be formed by lineage-committed progenitor cells with close to 100 percent cloning efficiency. Work with micromanipulated or FACS-sorted single cells had proved that colonies were clones formed by single cells. Such cultures could be performed using serum-free medium but the requirement to add "purified" bovine serum albumin to such cultures, with the consequent addition of many contaminating proteins to the culture, rendered such cultures far from the theoretically ideal state of having used fully characterized medium.

The period had seen the successful purification of seven hematopoietic regulators—erythropoietin, the four CSFs, IL-1, and IL-2. For the small number of laboratories possessing these purified regulators it was a golden time in which their actions could be established with some confidence.

We documented the existence of what appeared to be specific membrane receptors for the CSFs and made estimates of receptor numbers on responding cells. The answers emerging were somewhat astonishing in that, typically, only a few hundred receptors were present on individual cells and only a small fraction of these needed to be occupied to induce obvious cellular responses. At least in culture, active concentrations of regulators were in the sub-nanogram per milliliter range, making these regulators exceedingly high in their specific activity.

Certain features had emerged from the analysis of the functions of the CSFs that were regarded with some suspicion by workers in other fields and indeed some remain in dispute. The CSFs had been purified as simple growth factors, but analyses showed that each CSF was in fact polyfunctional with multiple distinct actions on hematopoietic cells. While the facts were clear enough, this conclusion was often met with polite disbelief by audiences. However, this principle is now a well-established fact for other growth factors—so much so that it has subsequently been claimed that the principle was known long before the work on the CSFs! This revisionist history does not fool those of us who were unfortunate enough to have given presentations on the multiple functions of the CSFs during this period.

Although polyfunctionality was disconcerting, in many ways it was a comfort because it offered some possibility of reducing the number of regulators likely to be necessary to control the complex processes by which one progenitor cell could generate a large number of mature, functionally active cells.

The initial observations made with the CSFs were that they appeared to be mandatory for cell division in cells of responding lineages, the concentration of the regulator determining cell cycle times and the total number of progeny produced in a defined period. This suggested strongly enough that the regulator was initiating a series of active responses in the proliferating cells but the molecular nature of these signals and responses would require a further decade to begin to be characterized.

There were, and still are, those who assumed that any normal mammalian cell can exhibit an intrinsic ability for unstimulated cell division—provided only that it is fed and kept healthy. This notion has proved unusually difficult to counter and, in the pre-1983 period, refutation was made more difficult by a second clear property of the CSFs. We and our colleagues in Rehovot had both noted that what came to be recognized as CSFs were needed to ensure the survival in culture of granulocyte-macrophage progenitor cells and their progeny. It is now known that in the absence of growth factors, hematopoietic cells die by apoptosis that has presumably been triggered by a failure of membrane transport systems in the cells. While this finding was an embarrassment for those of us claiming that proliferative stimulation was an active cellular process, it was nonetheless intriguing because the cellular events controlling survival were likely to be radically different from those controlling proliferation, yet the same molecule and receptor appeared to be involved.

A series of subsequent studies made it likely that CSFs had two additional actions. We found that where progenitor cells were bipotential, the CSF used to stimulate cell proliferation appeared to have some capacity to dictate what lineage the progeny entered. Somewhat similarly, other groups working with undifferentiated cell lines found that the addition of CSFs appeared able to trigger the commencement of maturation in these cell lines, even though the complex events required for maturation seemed unlikely to be able to be regulated in detail by a single molecule. Both these functions of the CSFs remain controversial. Differentiation commitment, particularly lineage commitment, may well be largely determined by other processes and the role played by the CSFs may be minor in its overall contribution. A decade later it was to be shown that, while CSF action can clearly initiate maturation in certain cell lines, it is equally clear that maturation can proceed to some degree without CSF action and that maturation can be initiated by a number of types of extraneously inserted unrelated receptors. This implies that CSF receptors have no unique role in initiating particular differentiation signals.

What was not in dispute was the fact noted by us through the initial work of Mathew Vadas and Angel Lopez and others that the CSFs can increase the functional activity of mature cells. Not all of the observed activations are unique for the CSFs because other agents can activate mature cells, but CSFs clearly have a powerful action.

The multiple biological actions able to be exhibited by a single type of regulator and its receptor raised problems regarding the manner in which signals could be initiated that needed to reach different parts of the cell to elicit these various responses. It would require much further work in the following 15 years before the structural architecture of the receptor that permits multiple signaling could begin to be documented.

Some initial studies had been carried out on the consequences of combining two or more regulators. Examples were documented where the combination of two CSFs produced superadditive proliferative responses—responses greater than achievable by twice the concentration of either CSF. The mechanisms responsible still remain partly unresolved. However, to begin to interpret such responses, it needed to be established that individual cells coexpressed receptors for more than one regulator. By 1983, such coexpression was able to be deduced from the types and frequency of ^{125}I-CSF binding cells noted by us, particularly for mature, readily identifiable cells. Proof that individual progenitor cells must coexpress multiple receptors had also been able to be deduced by us from studies in which clones initiated by one CSF could have their proliferation sustained after transfer to cultures containing another CSF. However, the extent of receptor coexpression and the cross-interactions exhibited by these receptors were not fully appreciated.

Regarding cellular sources of regulators, our initial expectations had been based to a degree on the single organ source of classical hormones and on evidence suggesting that erythropoietin was dominantly produced by the kidney.

The CSFs had proved to be radically different. To the extent we were able to analyze them, CSFs of one type or another appeared to be produced in every organ tested and the cell types able to be tested (including T lymphocytes, macrophages, fibroblasts, stromal cells, and epithelial cells) all exhibited a capacity to produce one or more CSF. This set a very different pattern but one that was later to become familiar when newer regulators were discovered. In this context, the behavior of Multi-CSF had been very puzzling. Although readily produced by activated T cells in vitro, it did not appear to be detectable in extracts of any normal mouse organs or in media produced in vitro by such organs, even those containing T lymphocytes. Subsequent work using much more sensitive bioassays and PCR analysis of organ cDNA has still failed to produce any evidence that cells produce this factor in the normal body.

It had been an appealing concept to many workers that regulator production might be triggered or controlled by the number of relevant mature cells present in the body. Consumption of CSFs by target cells had been documented by a number of groups and an extension of this concept to a more sophisticated receptor-mediated degradation would offer an intellectually satisfying method for at least modulating circulating regulator levels, although not providing a sensor mechanism for monitoring regulator levels or inducing new regulator production.

Initially, certain experiments of ours and others had seemed to support this type of model for the CSFs. Irradiation and cytotoxic drugs, which depleted granulocyte and macrophage numbers, had been observed to induce elevations in serum CSF levels. However, the initial studies had been performed using conventional animals and when they were repeated using germ-free animals or relatively clean animals, no such rises had been observed. Mature cell numbers therefore seemed to be an unsatisfactory mechanism for controlling CSF production. On the contrary, the marked responses of CSF levels to bacterial products we noted had favored an alternative proposal that CSF production was demand-generated by invading microorganisms. In this model, the products of microorganisms directly or indirectly induced CSF production, leading to granulocyte-macrophage activation or production of additional cells, with the inducing signal then being removed or diminished by the elimination of the microorganisms.

This then was the background information available regarding the CSFs at the termination of the phase of CSF purification, a time at which no tests had yet been possible on the effects of injected CSF in vivo or on the in vivo consequences of sustained increases or decreases in CSF levels. All the available biological information had been based on reductionist tissue cultures, and, although internally consistent models could be built up on how the CSFs might operate in the body, these were without direct experimental verification.

For some years, McCulloch's group in Toronto had been suggesting that the CSFs might be indeed in vitro artifacts. Perhaps only to be provocative, they proposed that the CSFs might merely be derived from shed membranes of cells and that their apparent proliferative effects in vitro really depended on inadequacies in the culture technique—a return to the original Puck proposal. There were data to support such a negative view because hematopoietic cells, particularly macrophages, are a good source of CSFs, as are lymphocytes. Membrane extracts made by the Toronto group deliberately for the purpose did seem to have proliferative actions in cultures of leukemic cells.

For those of us thinking in terms of secreted molecules, the notion that the active molecules were in fact possibly nonspecific membrane derivatives was difficult to accept but not easy to counter. Later events were to show that the two views were not mutually exclusive because M-CSF can be membrane-displayed, so membrane extracts would have activity. For a later discovered molecule, stem cell factor, the membrane-displayed form in fact was shown by David Williams and his group to be more effective than the secreted form. What really was unacceptable was the suggestion that CSFs were not specific regulatory molecules, although possibly our Canadian colleagues might not have intended to push this view quite so far.

The in vitro experiments had certainly aroused wide interest among hematologists and cell biologists, but this interest had been tempered by the quite valid reservations that there was as yet no evidence that the CSFs would exert comparable actions in vivo and, if they did, that they could be proved to be important regulators of granulocyte-macrophage populations in normal health or disease.

TEN

The Cloning of the CSF Genes

For all who had been involved in the purification of CSFs from native sources, one fact was overwhelming—that, even with enormous effort, only minute amounts of purified material could be produced. For many of our purposes in establishing the biological actions of the CSFs in vitro, these small amounts had sufficed for key experiments. However, the situation in 1983 was very gloomy. None of us could contemplate with equanimity the prospect of continuing to purify CSFs for decades simply to generate the same miserably small amounts of material. There had to be more to life than this.

Most impelling was the need to generate sufficient material to inject in vivo. After all, we had now been engaged in CSF work for 17 years and had yet to be able to inject a single mouse with pure CSF. There was no hard evidence that the CSFs and their observed actions were necessarily anything more than interesting in vitro artifacts.

The more astute among us came to the conclusion that the only way out of the logistical dilemma posed by the scarcity of CSF in normal tissues was to attempt to clone the genes encoding the CSFs and then to attempt the mass production of recombinant CSF using some suitable expression system.

While gene cloning procedures are now relatively simple and can be performed successfully by an average student, this was not the situation in 1983. Relatively few mammalian genes had been cloned and the required expertise was not widespread. Experience with the successful mass production of recombinant proteins using such cloned genes was even more limited and few examples could be produced to document the feasibility of such an approach. The level of thinking regarding the feasibility of these approaches in most academic laboratories was one of moderate theoretical enthusiasm, tempered by the rather daunting prospect of actually executing the whole maneuver.

What was not clearly appreciated by those in most academic laboratories was that some radical developments were beginning to occur with the setting up of commercially funded companies whose intent was to clone and express genes and thereby to generate funds to sustain their operation and further research. Most were initiated by the few academic scientists familiar with recombinant technology—indeed, often these were the originators of the technology and, therefore, true believers.

Oddly enough, these moves were not driven in a major manner by established pharmaceutical companies. On the whole, these established companies seemed even slower than academic scientists to see the possibilities emerging. The various embryonic gene cloning companies had a wide variety of candidate molecules in mind and not all had an interest in hematopoiesis or specifically in the hematopoietic regulators. Four of these, however, were to become dominant players in the field—Amgen (Thousand Oaks, CA), Immunex (Seattle, WA), DNAX (Palo Alto, CA), and Genetics Institute (Cambridge, MA). They actively recruited bright young molecular biologists and biochemists. Rather characteristically, they were understaffed in biologists but the intent was to cover the required biology by collaborative studies with the many biologists who would be eager to take on the task of characterizing the function of recombinant proteins. Few of these newly recruited scientists had previous experience in hematopoiesis, so these developments passed largely unnoticed by experimental hematologists.

From this time on, two competing streams of research, often on the same subjects, were to proceed almost totally independently except for a few scientists whose purified native proteins were initially needed to prime the company gene cloning programs.

For groups like our own who had began to seriously consider attempts to clone CSF genes, two approaches were possible in principle—cloning using nucleotide probes based on amino acid sequence data from the purified native molecules and, more adventurously, expression cloning using some suitable simple assay system with enough sensitivity to be able to detect the low concentrations of active material that might be able to be generated by gene pools also containing the gene of interest.

In pioneering studies that were to have an unexpected outcome, the first cloning of a cDNA for a hematopoietic regulator was actually achieved in 1980. Revel in Rehovot and his colleagues believed they had cloned a cDNA for interferon-$\beta 2$, a postulated member of a group of interferons with antiviral activity. In the following six years it became evident that interferon-$\beta 2$ was likely to be the same as a molecule being investigated as influencing the proliferation and maturation of B lymphocytes (BCDF or BSF-2). This was confirmed in 1986 when Kishimoto and his colleagues in Osaka cloned a cDNA for human BSF-2, and, because the actions of this molecule were becoming recognized to be broader than had been at first supposed, the name of the molecule was subsequently changed to interleukin-6 (IL-6). Two groups in 1988 reported the cloning of the corresponding cDNA for murine IL-6.

After this somewhat confusing beginning, the first formal cloning of a hematopoietic regulator was achieved in 1983 by Taniguchi and colleagues in Tokyo who cloned a cDNA for human IL-2. This had a startling effect on the field, the more so because it was achieved by the difficult maneuver of purifying IL-2 mRNA then hybridizing this to cDNA pools with injection of the material into frog oocytes to achieve production of biologically detectable IL-2. Two groups later cloned the corresponding cDNA for murine IL-2 in 1985.

It seemed as if cloning of cDNAs for various hematopoietic regulators was going to be feasible, we hoped by using the more direct methods of hybridization with sequence-based nucleotide probes or direct expression screening of cDNA pools. With this moral encouragement, the search for CSF cDNAs was begun by several groups, including our own, in 1983.

The Ludwig Institute/CSIRO team cloning murine granulocyte-macrophage colony-stimulating factor. Back row: Nick Gough, Tony Burgess, Ed Nice, and Ashley Dunn. Front row: Diane Grail, Jill Gough, and Lindsay Sparrow.

In October 1983 Fung and his colleagues at the Australian National University, Canberra, submitted a manuscript describing the successful cloning of murine IL-3 from a library constructed from mRNA from WEHI-3B cells. Within a week, Yokota and colleagues at DNAX submitted their manuscript also describing the isolation of a murine IL-3 cDNA from a library constructed from mRNA from a T-lymphocyte cell line. The pace of competitive discovery had certainly taken a major step forward and this was to set a pattern for events in the following years. Both groups had used a similar approach to that used for the cloning of IL-2 but employed highly responsive cell lines to detect the IL-3 being produced by oocytes injected with pooled cDNAs that had bound to purified mRNA preparations. The deduced sequences obtained by both groups contained the amino acid sequence obtained by Ihle's group for IL-3 purified from WEHI-3B-conditioned medium. Both papers appeared in print early in 1984 and this certainly increased the pressure on us.

In 1983, a team had been developed by us in Melbourne combining Ashley Dunn and Nick Gough and their molecular biology group in the Ludwig Institute for Cancer Research with our own biological and biochemical group in the adjacent Hall Institute. Our goal was to clone a cDNA for murine GM-CSF, making use of our available sequence data to construct redundant nucleotide probes that should have been adequate to identify GM-CSF cDNA.

Much of our work in cloning cDNAs was to be plagued by a recurring problem—the rather unsatisfactory sources of mRNA usually available to us for constructing cDNA libraries. Although particular cells or tissues could produce fairly large amounts of biological activity, this in fact represented relatively small numbers of protein molecules. These cellular sources therefore were not likely to be rich in CSF mRNA, so the resulting cDNA libraries would contain very few representatives of CSF cDNAs. Furthermore, in my view as a long-term observer of the molecular biology scene, a recurrent technical weakness in molecular biology is the variable quality of mRNA that can be extracted from tissues. We chose lung tissue from mice preinjected with endotoxin as the logical source for our mRNA, although we had no way of knowing at what precise time after injection mRNA levels might be at their highest. Clearly they would rise before levels of CSF protein, but how much earlier was unknown. We compromised by using tissue 3 and 15 hours after injection. Our misgivings about the likely frequency of CSF mRNA turned out to be well founded and our library in fact contained very few GM-CSF cDNA clones.

At the outset of this project, we had proposed these studies in an application for an NIH research grant, and, because of the usual delays in processing such grant applications, we had actually succeeded in cloning a GM-CSF cDNA before the dreaded pink report sheet reached us with the assessment of our application. Our application was approved but it contained a long and fairly accurate assessment of the difficulties we were likely to encounter based on calculations of the probable amounts of GM-CSF mRNA/cDNA we were likely to be able to use. Years later I met the scientist who had made this appraisal. He was kindly, unabashed, and I think delighted that we had succeeded despite his quite accurate predictions. From my viewpoint, this was a fine example of considered refereeing, with a carefully thought-through analysis indicating not much prospect of success but with a generous decision nonetheless to let us attempt the feat.

By using a cDNA library generated from mRNA, the hope is that most cDNAs in the library will be complete. However, reverse transcription has its limits and even if the mRNA had been intact, the copied cDNA is not necessarily complete. Our screening procedure worked well enough in that the probes were of sufficient specificity to survive stringent washing, but the best candidate for a GM-CSF cDNA clone that we obtained turned out to be incomplete, with no possibility of generating a protein product. To verify that this incomplete cDNA did indeed encode portion of the GM-CSF molecule, we then also had to resort to the maneuver of allowing the cDNA fragment to hybridize with further lung-derived mRNA in the hope of capturing enough complete GM-CSF mRNA to then inject into frog oocytes, which we hoped would result in sufficient GM-CSF production to be detectable.

Fortunately for us, we had now begun using microwell assays of granulocyte-macrophage progenitor cells purified by Nick Nicola by fluorescence-activated cell sorting (FACS) of mouse fetal liver cells. The survival and proliferation of these cells in culture can be stimulated by very low concentrations of GM-CSF. In these microwell assays, low GM-CSF concentrations produce obvious proliferation of the 200 cells added to each well. With no CSF, no cells survive, and with minute GM-CSF concentrations, survival of some of these cells occurs but with no proliferation. This was the system in which our oocyte-conditioned medium was tested. Most batches were negative with no surviving cells after two days of incubation. With one batch, however, a total of six cells seemed to be viable. With my heart in my mouth, I gave my molecular biology colleagues a report that this material was probably active and that they might well have in their possession a partial GM-CSF cDNA clone. Never has so much depended on so few cells.

Armed with this slim evidence that the incomplete clone was probably correct, we rehybridized this incomplete cDNA with mRNA from a T-lymphocyte cell line that had been shown to be a very rich source of GM-CSF. This time the oocyte-conditioned media had much more convincing CSF activity. A second more complete cDNA clone was isolated, which when combined with the overlapping original clone

The Hall Institute biological and biochemical team assisting in cloning murine GM-CSF. Back row: Luba Oddo, Don Metcalf, Annette Futter, Nick Nicola, and Anne Kelso. Front row: Yvonne Wiluszynski and Cathy Quilici.

seemed to represent a complete GM-CSF cDNA. This cDNA would encode a polypeptide whose sequence included that obtained by partial sequencing of the purified native molecule. Subsequently, a full-length cDNA was isolated from a T lymphocyte-derived library using the original incomplete cDNA clone as a probe. This complete cDNA was then used in a transient expression system to produce recombinant GM-CSF with all the properties of native GM-CSF.

In parallel with our publication in 1984 of the successful cloning of a cDNA for murine GM-CSF, a patent application was lodged. Responsibility for patenting the murine GM-CSF cDNA was delegated to the Ludwig Institute, with any resulting royalties to be split 50-50 between the Hall Institute and the Ludwig Institute. The Ludwig Institute in turn passed the handling and development of GM-CSF to Research Corporation Technologies (Tucson, Arizona), which would first take 40 percent of all royalties before passing the residue to the two institutes. Our murine patent application was never seriously challenged. What was challenged was whether such a murine patent had dominance over subsequent patent applications for human GM-CSF. These patent proceedings were to drag on in the United States at much expense for more than a decade before we were successful in winning the human patent in 1997. What seemed partly responsible for the protracted proceedings was that this seemed to be the first, precedent-setting occasion on which this general issue needed to be resolved. More obvious, however, were interference proceedings initiated by a number of companies that felt that they had a better claim to the human GM-CSF patent, even though these patent applications had been lodged some time after ours.

Gordon Wong and his colleagues at Genetics Institute had been attempting to clone a human GM-CSF during the same period in which we had been cloning murine GM-CSF. Publication of our work in *Nature* came as an unpleasant surprise to them. They had begun in a similar manner to us, using human GM-CSF purified by David Golde's group in Los Angeles from medium conditioned by the human MO hairy cell leukemia cell line. Their approach used sequence data from this material, but the synthesized nucleotide probes had not been successful in isolating a cDNA clone and they turned to expression screening, with a bioassay using a CSF-dependent human leukemic cell line. This approach ultimately succeeded in isolating a human GM-CSF cDNA and the deduced amino acid sequence for this cDNA included the sequence they had obtained from purified native GM-CSF. While different from the murine GM-CSF, there was some degree of homology shown by the human GM-CSF and the data were published in 1985.

Using much the same expression screening approach, Frank Lee and his group at DNAX also succeeded in isolating a cDNA for human GM-CSF, also publishing their data in 1985.

Michael Cantrell and his colleagues at Immunex adopted a more direct approach by isolating a murine cDNA using our published sequence and then used this as a probe to screen human cDNA libraries by cross-hybridization. Again, they were successful in isolating a cDNA that, on expression, appeared to code for the production of a molecule with the properties expected of human GM-CSF and again the publication appeared in 1985.

We had arranged to undertake collaborative studies with Schering Plough (Rahway, New Jersey) where their goal was to clone a corresponding human GM-CSF cDNA. Their progress was slow but ultimately successful.

These were the serious contestants over the next 12 years for the human GM-CSF patent. Immunex appeared to have no likely chance of success but the greatest incentive to prolong the proceedings because, during this period, their recombinant human GM-CSF had been clinically tested and licensed for clinical use. Because payment of royalties is not retrospective, any delay incurred in assigning a patent saved them from possible royalty payments and more than compensated them for the costs of legal proceedings.

At least in Europe, Schering and Sandoz (Basel/Vienna) did team up to develop GM-CSF with the recombinant GM-CSF being produced by Schering in Ireland. These companies also carried out successful clinical trials and won licenses for some clinical uses in Europe.

What a group chooses to do when a murine cDNA has been obtained that encodes a candidate regulatory factor depends very much on the motivations behind the group's studies. Academic laboratories were possibly very naive in not placing clinical use and financial reward at the top of their motivation lists. This was obviously not the case with gene cloning companies like Genetics Institute or Immunex. They wanted a product for clinical use and financial reward. This was their *raison d'être*. In this they were also demonstrating naïveity and an almost touching belief in what they had heard being described and discussed by us at numerous meetings in the preceding decade. We basic scientists had in a sense been our own worst enemies in popularizing the CSFs as likely regulators. Our stories were accurate enough descriptions of our in vitro experiments but these were merely in vitro experiments and we, at least, had considerable reservations about whether the CSFs would function in a useful manner when injected in vivo.

To dismiss these uncertainties and "go for gold" may have been a very sensible decision on the part of the scientists and development teams in these companies. History shows that they were quite correct in their leap of faith for two of the CSFs, but possibly were premature with other hematopoietic regulators when using the same jugular approach.

In truth, no one in the period from 1983 to 1985 had any firm grounds for expecting that recombinant CSFs would be billion-dollar clinical agents, so, in working on this basis, the company scientists were displaying considerable initiative and academic scientists were on the whole being rather naïve. Academic scientists are, however, fast learners and the experience with recombinant erythropoietin, GM-CSF, and G-CSF induced a sharp change in their behavior on later occasions.

What were our own reactions and expectations in 1984, having cloned a cDNA for our long-term companion, GM-CSF? Our behavior within our group very much reflected our differing background expertise and intellectual goals. Our molecular biology colleagues became intrigued by the structure of the cDNA, spent time establishing the chromosomal location of this gene, and expended much effort establishing the chromosomal structure of the gene. For them, these were key pieces of information needed for longer-term studies on genetically manipulated mice—either transgenic or gene-inactivated. With the small numbers of their staff, these matters essentially fully occupied them to the exclusion of deploying much effort to clone a cDNA for human GM-CSF by homology screening or to clone murine G-CSF using sequence data that were becoming available from the sequencing of our purified murine G-CSF. I must confess that we felt very frustrated by our inability to persuade our molecular biology colleagues to put effort into a G-CSF cloning project and resolved, as soon as possible, to set up our own molecular biology group where urgent projects could be more effectively initiated.

My own initial reactions to success in cloning a cDNA for GM-CSF were pleasure at a successful technical feat but also overwhelming relief that a mammalian gene for GM-CSF actually existed. Throughout all the years of purification of GM-CSF, it had been a private nagging fear that GM-CSF might actually be a microbial product from contamination of our production sources. To find that our 15 years of effort had not been a waste of time, not so much for analyzing hematopoietic biology but for characterizing a genuine cellular product, was an overwhelming relief. The biologists in the group did appreciate that there was going to be a delay in mass-producing biologically active recombinant CSF, but, given reasonable luck, this might now be possible. If so, we could at last envisage the day approaching when recombinant CSF could be injected in vivo to establish whether any changes were inducible in granulocyte-macrophage populations.

The exercise of producing a recombinant product using a cDNA clone has now become fairly trivial, or, if never entirely trivial, at least a well-established maneuver—the sort of task a bright student should be able to accomplish with a little guidance. This was not the situation in 1984. Successful experience in producing recombinant proteins was not extensive and the available expression systems were relatively limited and not particularly efficient. It was easy enough to obtain small amounts of material using transient expression systems but to mass-produce then purify milligram amounts was entirely another matter. These were the amounts that clearly were going to be required for even a modest in vivo testing program in mice.

We therefore had to seek collaborative assistance from an industrial group able to undertake such a project. Those already known to be engaged in their own CSF cloning programs were obviously not available for such an approach. It was at this point that the general lack of appreciation that CSFs might be commercially valuable became evident from the general reluctance of established pharmaceutical companies to enter into what was still a speculative exercise.

We tried unsuccessfully to arrange a program of recombinant CSF production with the only available biotechnology company in Australia, Biotechnology Australia, but interest was lukewarm and their resources were fully committed. We turned eventually to Biogen, Geneva, for collaborative assistance. This company had talented scientists and expertise but was not a particularly dynamic organization. However, John DeLamarter and his group did take our GM-CSF project on board, running at the same time a similar project to mass-produce murine IL-3. Their progress seemed slow to us but these were early days in the development of recombinant technology and they had no other option than to use expression systems that have now been superseded. Biogen researchers were eventually successful in mass-producing recombinant murine IL-3 and GM-CSF.

With murine IL-3 and GM-CSF successfully cloned and produced in bioactive recombinant form, attention turned to M-CSF and G-CSF.

Cloning of a cDNA for human M-CSF was carried out by Kawasaki and colleagues at Cetus (CA) in collaboration with Richard Stanley. Cetus used nucleotide probes based on sequence data from human urine M-CSF purified by Richard Stanley. Publication of this cloning also occurred in 1985. Subsequently, in 1988, Wong and colleagues at Genetics Institute published the isolation of a somewhat different cDNA for human M-CSF. Three groups reported in 1987 the isolation of cDNAs for murine M-CSF.

Meantime, powerful groups at Amgen and Chugai (Tokyo) had been working hard to be the first to purify human G-CSF and, with the resulting sequence data, to develop nucleotide probes to clone a cDNA for G-CSF. It is interesting that both groups were working with G-CSF produced by human neoplastic cell lines—a bladder carcinoma cell line, 5637 in the case of the New York–Amgen group and a squamous carcinoma cell line, CHU-2, in the case of the Japanese workers. The Amgen group under Larry Souza was using CSF that had been purified by Malcolm Moore's group at the Sloan-Kettering Institute, New York, in the mistaken belief that they were purifying a pluripoietin, possibly of IL-3 type. We had pointed out to Karl Welte and Erich Platzer, the two German postdocs doing this work, that, from its biochemical properties, the material seemed to resemble G-CSF. If, as they believed at the time, the material also stimulated eosinophil colony formation, it might still be contaminated with some GM-CSF that had been present in the original tumor cell conditioned medium. Amgen was unable to obtain usable sequence data from the original New York material and set to work repurifying the CSF preparation. They then were successful in obtaining adequate sequence data, developing suitable nucleotide probes, and in cloning a cDNA for G-CSF.

Shige Nagata and his group in Tokyo together with a group at Chugai made use of G-CSF purified from CHU-2 cells, derived adequate sequence data to allow the synthesis of nucleotide probes then successfully cloned a cDNA, which, on expression, generated material with the properties of G-CSF. Both groups published the successful cloning of cDNA for human G-CSF in 1986 and later in the same year Nagata and colleagues cloned a cDNA for murine G-CSF.

In an unkind little twist of fate, while we were sequencing our murine G-CSF as an initial step in attempting to clone a murine G-CSF cDNA, I received for refereeing from *Nature* the manuscript of Nagata and colleagues describing the successful cloning of human G-CSF. This bombshell very effectively ended our attempts to clone G-CSF because the data from the human G-CSF sequence were clearly related to our murine G-CSF sequence data. My disappointment was short-lived and I spent the evening rewriting some of the English of the manuscript so that it would read more clearly on publication. At that stage no one realized fully what a major money-spinner G-CSF would become. Even if I had, an excellent piece of research is still excellent and warrants every assistance in ensuring publication.

Both the Chugai and Amgen groups promptly filed patent applications, which were again to be the subject of prolonged disputation at the U.S. Patent Office. While this disputation phase was in progress, both products had successfully passed through clinical trials and had been licensed for certain clinical uses. Clearly the patent disputation was now potentially involving very large sums of money in anticipated sales. Various experts on G-CSF, including our own group, were approached for opinions regarding the relative merits of the two claims and what exactly was being specified in them. Any inexactitude or errors in such patent applications can provide ammunition for an opposing group and the resolution of such disputes is certainly not simply a matter of the priority of filing dates. The disputation was finally settled out of court with an agreed arrangement in which Amgen had rights to the U.S. market and Chugai rights to the Japanese market while both parties competed on equal terms in Europe and elsewhere.

Amgen, Chugai, and Immunex differed radically from other companies in their performance during the developmental stages. Their intent was to develop into major pharmaceutical companies based on the successful development, testing, and sale for human use of their recombinant products and their animal trials, toxicity tests, and clinical trials were performed in a highly competent manner. Amgen has since forged ahead to be a major company based mainly on two highly successful products, erythropoietin and G-CSF, both billion-dollar-a-year products. Immunex managed to create a viable enough pharmaceutical company based on GM-CSF but with far smaller sales than achieved by

Amgen. Chugai, as a pharmaceutical company, had other products but G-CSF certainly was to prove a major product for them.

The cloning of a cDNA for human Multi-CSF (IL-3) proved particularly difficult for Yu-Chun Yang and her group at Genetics Institute because of major differences in the protein sequence between murine and human IL-3. It was a tour de force to finally isolate a cDNA for human IL-3 by first isolating a partially cross-reactive clone for gibbon IL-3 then using this clone to isolate a cross-reactive human clone. This success was also published in 1986.

Thus in the three-year period from 1984 to 1986, the successful isolation of cDNAs, either human or murine, had been reported for all four CSFs and shortly thereafter useful amounts of recombinant CSF began to be produced.

This surge of cloning work with CSF cDNAs was to set a precedent for what was to follow with many subsequently described hematopoietic regulators. Although there were some exceptions, more and more of these newer regulators were first produced in recombinant form, without the prior effort of purifying the corresponding native molecules. For those confronted with a possibly new regulator in crude material, there is now a very real decision required as to how to proceed—the slow purification route or the potentially quicker cloning route? Either way, recombinant regulators now tend to appear on the scene with essentially no background information on their likely function in vivo or even much information on their biological actions in vitro.

Equally dramatic had been the impact of the entry of a new force into biological work of this type. The gene cloning companies were now determined to make their own primary discoveries and not rely simply on discoveries made in some academic laboratory, which were then turned over to them for development. To achieve this, they expanded into what amounted to large new research institutes, highly focused in the area of regulator biology—probably more than doubling the workforce of existing scientists in the field. The company scientists were supported entirely by company funds, and, as a consequence, where a company had products to sell, the prices were set to cover research expenses. In this situation, the public had become at considerable risk of paying twice for particular research progress—once via taxes to support grant-funded research and a second time through the cost of more expensive clinical products.

Simultaneous discoveries in academic science were by now becoming quite common but the duplicative studies of company scientists were much more evident. It was becoming exceedingly difficult for an academic scientist to discover anything that might not be simultaneously worked on by other, usually larger, groups. The competitive pressure on scientists post-1986 has become extreme, the more so since there is the ever-present hope for yet another pot of gold like erythropoietin or G-CSF. The response to this pressure has varied. Some academic groups have essentially conceded defeat and moved to other areas. Groups like ours that are relatively large now need to be able to accelerate projects promptly when promising candidates appear for possible exploitation. More than ever before, creative science has become a group exercise. This was inevitable given the increasing complexity of the technology in use. However, to the competitive nature of science that is discovery-based, now are added the twin elements of likely simultaneous discoveries by large numbers of workers in our field as well as the evident risk of company-based highly focused competition.

Work on a new candidate regulator can no longer be left in the unaided hands of a Ph.D. student who may have made the initial observation, because the work needs to be quickly transferred to a balanced team of experts. Not all students are able to accept this loss of personal property, even if they subsequently feature as first author on a substantial publication, although some relish the excitement and bustle of a group working on their project. Because such projects are high-risk, and we have had experience of student discomfiture, we would certainly not now assign such a project to a student where there seemed some likelihood that, before long, it might need to be fast-tracked.

This has tended to remove one of the main satisfactions for a young scientist—the hope that they too will make a solo discovery of importance. Because everyone is now in the same boat, events are showing that the career of a good young scientist will in fact prosper more rapidly in such a group context if care is taken to preserve the rights of the young colleague in terms of publication record and performance at scientific meetings. This is because the written or oral presentations will contain much more information than could possibly have been acquired by a single investigator. For all of us, the days have passed when preliminary or incomplete studies, of the type in our early publications on the purification of CSFs, are now acceptable to journals or referees and complete studies need multiple pairs of hands and a multidisciplinary approach.

Perhaps these changes would have happened inevitably with the increasing sophistication of experimental biology, but they were radically accelerated by the entry of molecular biology into experimental hematopoiesis, particularly when some of the products became of obvious clinical and commercial value.

ELEVEN

The Recombinant CSFs In Vitro and at Last In Vivo

As soon as CSF cDNAs were cloned, it became possible for the groups involved to verify that the biological actions in vitro of the recombinant CSFs paralleled the known actions of the native molecules. It was possible to establish this quite quickly using transient expression systems able to produce small amounts of recombinant material. In the case of each CSF, the recombinant equivalent seemed able to reproduce qualitatively all the actions of the native molecules. In the main, this preliminary information was included in the initial publications describing the cloning of the cDNAs.

More formal tests on purified recombinant CSF were not such a trivial exercise and required the production and purification of substantial milligram amounts of material. These were 1,000-fold more than the amounts ever able to be purified from native sources. If the material proved satisfactory, the way was open to perform large-scale studies in vitro and, more important, to investigate the effects of injected CSF in mice or other animals.

For each CSF, there were basically three options available—mammalian expression systems, producing glycosylated material that one hoped would fairly closely resemble the native CSF molecule; yeast expression systems, again producing glycosylated material but with a somewhat excessive and possibly abnormal carbohydrate component;

and bacterial expression systems, producing CSF that lacked carbohydrate. It had already been established from in vitro work on native CSFs that the carbohydrate component could be removed without loss of biological activity, but the consequences of hyperglycosylation were unknown.

Eventually, most versions of recombinant CSFs were produced and, after purification, not only exhibited the same qualitative actions as the native molecules but closely similar quantitative bioactivity per milligram of protein. We had paid particular attention to recombinant GM-CSF, both murine and human, the latter supplied initially by Genetics Institute, and could find no differences from native GM-CSF except that nonglycosylated recombinant GM-CSF could have a specific activity up to 10 times higher than that of the native or recombinant glycosylated GM-CSF. We later carried out a similar detailed quantitative comparison of purified native Multi-CSF with recombinant IL-3 (Multi-CSF) paying particular attention that all the multiple actions of Multi-CSFs were in fact faithfully reproduced by the recombinant material. The only oddity about recombinant Multi-CSF was its tendency to lose biological activity unless carefully stored, presumably due to some instability in the refolding of the recombinant protein. In other laboratories, similar comparative analyses verified that recombinant M-CSF and G-CSF were indistinguishable in their properties from the native molecules.

We therefore felt confident that recombinant CSFs could be substituted for native CSFs for all future in vitro studies, relieving us from the tedium of further purification of native molecules.

CSF Synergy and Redundancy

From the biological point of view, the mass production of recombinant hematopoietic regulators meant that many laboratories previously working on cellular hematopoiesis in vitro could now buy or beg recombinant reagents for use in their studies. There was an abrupt rise in publications using purified regulators to establish their precise in vitro actions.

Several matters became evident during this period. Individual progenitor cells did indeed simultaneously co-express receptors for more than one regulator as did their maturing progeny. The design system of regulatory control seemed likely to call for cooperation between such regulators, at least in certain situations.

This immediately raised in some minds an alternative view that a regulatory system in which four CSFs could exert fairly comparable actions on the same cells had to be one that was highly redundant. It was suggested that some of these CSFs (and other agents beginning to appear that also had actions on granulocytic populations, like IL-6 and stem cell factor) were likely to be functionally unnecessary or inactive—perhaps representing no more than the genetic debris of earlier life forms in which they may have had an exclusive or major role but one that had now been superseded. This redundancy issue became so entrenched that it was to lead eventually to a new phase in work on the CSFs in which animals had to be developed that lacked individual genes of this group.

For those of us who accepted the existence of multiple regulators with more equanimity, the reasons for this arrangement were sought. In vitro studies by us and other groups revealed that, when stimulating progenitor cell proliferation, combinations of CSFs or of CSFs with other agents could result in superadditive proliferative responses. The action of regulators, when in combination, therefore seemed likely to achieve a significant economy in that lower concentrations of individual regulators, when combined, could achieve the same level of cell proliferation. Furthermore, because the exact mix of progeny produced in the granulocyte-macrophage or eosinophil lineages could be skewed by appropriate regulator combinations, such an arrangement would have the ability to generate slightly different population mixes of mature cells that might well be more effective at various stages in different infections. Combinations of regulators clearly could achieve a more sophisticated outcome than that achievable by the use of a single regulator. The potential advantages of combinations were to become even more obvious when studies were commenced on the in vivo effects of the CSFs.

The intracellular mechanisms responsible for superadditive synergistic responses are still not fully understood. Individual receptors, when occupied, can reduce the capacity of cells to bind certain other regulators even though the numbers of such receptors are small on individual cells. This almost certainly requires that the receptors are aggregated in islands on the cell membrane. This phenomenon should actually result in subadditive responses, not superadditive synergy. Conversely, however, certain regulators can increase expression of membrane receptors for other regulators, a response that would encourage amplified responsiveness. Although different receptors have differing signaling intracytoplasmic domains, it is believed that only a single final common pathway exists for mitotic signaling. If so, then to obtain responses that are superadditive suggests that signaling from some receptors may become restricted by a shortage of various activated signaling intermediates and possibly this can be supplemented by cascades of activated intermediates from other types of receptor.

In our work with murine progenitor cell responses, it became evident that, when GM-CSF and M-CSF were combined, certain types of very large granulocyte-macrophage or macrophage colonies developed that could not be induced to develop simply by doubling the concentration either of GM-CSF or M-CSF. There appeared therefore to be a subset of progenitor cells that actually required simultaneous stimulation by two regulators before beginning to proliferate. At the same time we and others, using FACS-purified stem cell populations, found that these cells would not respond by proliferation when stimulated by single regulators such as the CSFs or newer agents like IL-6, SCF, or FL. However, such cells were able to form colonies in vitro if stimulated by cocktails of such factors, leading to the recognition of a major difference between stem and progenitor cells in their responsiveness to single versus multiple regulators. These observations should have led to the abandonment of charges of hematopoietic regulator redundancy, but such claims persisted.

These interactions added a new dimension to work on the CSFs because now it needed to be envisaged that, when the CSFs were injected in vivo, they might interact with other regulators and might even depend heavily on these interactions for any responses elicited. It was going to be very difficult to determine precisely what actions of injected CSF were ascribable to direct effects of the CSF and what to combined interactions of the injected CSF with other regulators.

In Vivo Actions of the CSFs

With some of this information established from initial in vitro experiments during this period, we now were confident that it would be valid for recombinant CSF to be used in formal studies on the actions of injected CSF in animals. There was already information that nonglycosylated erythropoietin was not effective in vivo because of its exceptionally rapid clearance, so we did have some reservations about using nonglycosylated CSFs in vivo. However, events showed that the CSFs appeared to be reasonably equivalent in their behavior in vivo whether glycosylated or nonglycosylated.

It is a curious fact that essentially all in vivo testing of the CSFs in animals and later in humans was to involve the use of recombinant CSFs. One exception was a small-scale testing of human urinary M-CSF in patients in Japan, but, with this exception, everything now known about the behavior of injected CSFs has carried with it the presumption that native CSFs would have behaved in exactly the same manner.

Prior to the first experiments injecting CSF in vivo, three pessimistic predictions had been made fairly often by others. First, in view of the complex, potentially self-adjusting, regulatory networks whose existence had been suggested by individual in vitro experiments, it was predicted that no detectable response would occur in vivo following the injection of a single regulatory factor. Second, it was also predicted that the injected regulator would never be able to penetrate the tightly packed marrow population to achieve any significant increase in the concentration of that regulator above that already present as a result of endogenous production in such local regions. Finally, if responses were to occur, they would be of quite transient duration simply because the CSFs would stimulate existing progenitor cells to expend themselves by generating mature progeny cells, which would then result in a hiatus in cell production.

In the event, none of these predictions proved true.

We were dependent on Biogen for the necessary supplies of purified recombinant CSF and, after what seemed to us an interminable delay, a first small shipment of IL-3 arrived. Supplies of murine IL-3 had also been made available by Biogen to a Swiss group.

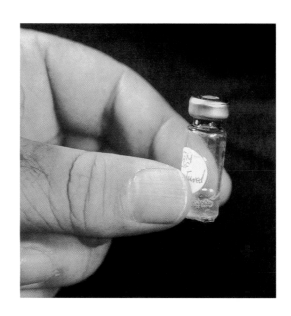

The world's first recombinant murine GM-CSF about to be processed before injecting into mice.

Our first in vivo tests on the IL-3 supplied in April 1985 were an ill-conceived attempt, using a few nude mice with Mesocestoides corti infection, to promote a local peritoneal eosinophil response, typical of that seen in normal infested mice. The attempt was premature and no response was noted.

Shortly after this abortive beginning, supplies of recombinant murine GM-CSF arrived. Although purified, we subjected the material to further refractionation to remove any toxic material of bacterial origin that might have been present and took care to establish that the material was free of endotoxin. We also initially used additional mice injected with small amounts of endotoxin as a further control against getting possibly misleading results.

So in May 1985 we began our long-awaited tests on murine GM-CSF in mice, almost exactly 20 years after commencing work on the CSFs. It was a time of tense anticipation to say the least.

To this point our expectations had been based wholly on the relative in vitro bioactivity shown by the CSFs. In terms of the numbers and size of colonies able to be stimulated in culture by added CSFs, a very clear order of activity was well recognized. IL-3 and GM-CSF appeared to be the most active and the most appealing because of their action on granulocytes, macrophages, and eosinophils with, for IL-3, the added attraction of stimulating megakaryocyte and possibly erythroid and mast cell proliferation. Murine M-CSF was a strong enough stimulus but fairly restricted to macrophage populations. In contrast, little expectation was held for G-CSF, which, in murine cultures, appeared not only to be a feeble proliferative stimulus but to be able to stimulate the proliferation of only a small subset of granulocyte precursors. Experience was to show that, when tested in mice, although the lineage specificity of action was maintained, the magnitude of effects inducible in vivo by the CSFs was almost the inverse of their in vitro activity.

We had decided to use a more sensible course of injections for six days with a formal analysis of the adult mice on the seventh day. We were quite uncertain regarding the half-life in vivo of the nonglycosylated GM-CSF, the best route of injection, and the frequency with which injections would need to be given to maintain reasonable serum concentrations of GM-CSF. We therefore initially made time-course studies to determine the levels of GM-CSF and their duration attainable by subcutaneous, intraperitoneal, or intravenous injections. We opted eventually to use intraperitoneal injections because they achieved levels that were intermediate between those attainable using the other routes and because intraperitoneal injections were more practicable if multiple injections were going to be necessary, often being given at night by a single person. The protocol we chose was three injections per day, but this was far from ideal because there would be longish intervals between injections when no circulating GM-CSF was detectable by bioassay. Perhaps, today, we would have opted for subcutaneous injections that sustain levels a little better or would have implanted small capsules delivering a more constant amount of CSF by osmotic pump action. In the event, the responses noted would not have been very different. Use of the intraperitoneal route for testing GM-CSF proved to be a fortunate choice.

After six days of injections of up to 200 ng per injection to adult mice, responses in the blood were disappointingly small with only twofold rises in neutrophil levels. However, the next procedure in working up these mice was to perform peritoneal cell counts—the local site of the GM-CSF injections. This for me was the tensest time in the past 20 years of effort. Was there going to be some major change or not? We were dealing with an agent undoubtedly present in the body, but were the in vitro data going to prove to be completely misleading or was the body's regulatory system far too complex to be perturbed by injecting a single regulator?

During the performance of the white cell counts, the top of a glass Pasteur pipette had snapped off and by chance had fallen into my shoe and seemed to have become embedded in my big toe. So intense was my anxiety and hope for something to be observable in these mice, I could not bear to stop and remove this impacted piece of glass. When Cathy Quilici, who was helping me with these experiments, removed the fluid from the peritoneal cavity of the first mouse injected with GM-CSF, instead of the fluid being as usual merely transparent like the injected harvest fluid, the fluid aspirated from the cavity was opalescent due to increased cell numbers—as was the fluid from the next mouse and the next.

At this point, I felt an enormous surge of relief. We had achieved a quite unequivocal in vivo response, and I clearly recollect saying to myself at this point that if this could be achieved in a mouse, then somewhere, in some type of patient, the CSFs were going to be clinically useful. I felt privileged to have witnessed a dramatic event of the type that is very uncommon in experimental medicine. I felt that a large part of our job with GM-CSF might well now be complete and certainly that it was time to pause, take off my shoe, and remove the impacted piece of glass.

With the doses of GM-CSF we felt able to use at that time, peripheral blood responses had been very small but GM-CSF was reproducibly able to induce 10- to 100-fold rises in various cell types in the peritoneal cavity, with the most prominent population, the macrophages, clearly exhibiting local proliferation with mitotic figures. Changes in other organs were much less dramatic although there was a 50 percent rise in spleen weight with a doubling of megakaryocyte numbers and progenitor cell content. Tests showed that the peritoneal macrophages had been functionally activated by the GM-CSF injections.

We concluded that injections of GM-CSF were able to achieve reproducible responses in the expected cell types but that, with the doses used, local responses were more prominent than systemic responses.

At this stage, a hiatus occurred with our supplies of GM-CSF and our studies on GM-CSF were not completed until May 1986, with publication of the results not appearing in *Experimental Hematology* until January 1987. While the work with GM-CSF was proceeding, more supplies of IL-3 had arrived and for much of the latter half of 1985, in vivo trials of GM-CSF and IL-3 were run in parallel.

With IL-3 (Multi-CSF) we again explored the various possible routes of injection and again settled on the intraperitoneal route with six days of injection. As was the case with GM-CSF, there were changes to be observed in mice injected with IL-3, but careful analysis was required to reveal them. It was again not simply a matter of performing white cell counts on the blood to establish what might have happened.

In the blood, eosinophil levels were elevated 10-fold and neutrophil and monocyte levels 2- to 3-fold. No significant changes were observed in the marrow but spleen size was increased 50 percent and the organ contained increased numbers of nonlymphoid hematopoietic cells with a 6- to 18-fold rise in progenitor cell numbers. The cell type exhibiting the largest numerical rise was mast cells whose numbers in the spleen rose 100-fold, and responses in this population turned out to be the most sensitive parameter for detecting responses to IL-3. This presaged that problems might arise due to such mast cells when trials were performed in humans, and this turned out to be the case. In the peritoneal cavity, there was also a 6- to 15-fold rise in cellular content and tests showed that both the neutrophils and macrophages had been functionally activated.

These findings were published in 1986 and this paper contained what I think was our first published statement that the injection of CSFs should be useful clinically to stimulate hematopoiesis. Together with a briefer report in 1986 from Kindler and colleagues in Geneva on progenitor cell changes in IL-3-injected mice, they represented the first published evidence that the injection of purified CSF into mice could induce changes in hematopoietic populations. Moreover, the cell types responding were those expected to be responsive from in vitro studies.

The results with injected IL-3 and GM-CSF were real enough in terms of moderately increased cell production with evidence for activation of mature cells in vivo, but I must confess that I soon became slightly disappointed that they had not been of larger magnitude. Later studies were to show that when higher concentrations of these CSFs were involved, both agents could produce marked elevations in granulocyte, monocyte, and eosinophil levels. However this reassurance was to come two years later.

When recombinant G-CSF was able to be produced by Amgen and Chugai, events began to move very rapidly. None of us had held out too much hope for G-CSF but this agent was to prove to elicit readily detectable responses of impressive magnitude. Following the injection of G-CSF, blood neutrophil levels became elevated to astonishing levels, almost 100-fold above those in control animals. This was accompanied by a very obvious accumulation of less mature granulocytic populations in the marrow and in the enlarging spleen. Indeed, so extreme were these changes in the marrow that the erythroid populations actually became displaced to the spleen.

With the close similarity between G-CSF in different species, all manner of animals including primates were found to exhibit comparable responses. We certainly envied our colleagues who were able to achieve such dramatic responses but rejoiced that at least one of our CSFs was proving to have absolutely unequivocal actions in vivo.

The dramatic success of G-CSF coming on top of more modest responses achievable by IL-3 and GM-CSF were fortunate in one respect. When M-CSF was tested in vivo somewhat later, the responses were relatively poor and often no more than a slight increase in the percentage of monocytes in the blood. In view of subsequent work with M-CSF, to be described later, this indifferent response to injected M-CSF is actually quite puzzling.

Against predictions, responses to injected CSF could readily be sustained for as long as injections were continued. No period was noted when progenitor cell numbers were significantly reduced—indeed these cells typically increased in number with time.

Further experiments were to show that the sustained responses to injected CSF, and in particular the unusually strong responses to G-CSF, were based in part on the ability of the injected CSF to increase progenitor cell production by stem cells. In this action, the CSF needs to interact with other regulators in the body, particularly with stem cell factor. In mice lacking stem cell factor, responses to injected G-CSF were relatively poor.

It needs to be added in parenthesis that when later hematopoietic regulators like stem cell factor or IL-6 were injected into mice, the observed responses were very small. This suggested that the CSFs were likely to be the major regulators of granulocyte-macrophage populations, as had appeared to be the case from earlier in vitro studies.

In total, the tests on the effects of injected CSFs in animals revealed each to have measurable effects, granted of widely varying magnitude. These effects were the sustained stimulation of cell proliferation, as measured by the increased production and numbers of mature cells in the blood and tissues, and functional activation of the mature cells. The cells involved in these responses were those expected to respond from in vitro studies. The different CSFs exhibited some differences in the tissue location of the most obvious responses, adding a new parameter to the subtle differences achievable with each CSF.

We performed some of the few experiments in mice where combinations of CSFs were injected. These revealed some examples of synergy but also produced evidence that the characteristic pattern of responses to each CSF was retained when combinations were injected.

It was a logical next step in these in vivo experiments to determine whether CSF injections could accelerate the regeneration of granulocyte-macrophage populations after damage of the host hematopoietic tissues by the administration of irradiation or cytotoxic drugs. These were obvious key studies to be performed if the CSFs were to be of clinical value. In general, CSF injections, again most evident with G-CSF, were able to accelerate the regeneration of hematopoietic populations under these conditions.

The second logical question to investigate was whether the injection of CSFs could enhance resistance to infections of one type or another.

A clinical correlation, well established early in the century, was that persons with low blood neutrophil levels were particularly susceptible to bacterial and fungal infections and, once infected, had difficulty in controlling the infection. This situation did not change completely with the introduction of antibiotics. From these facts, it could be proposed that if methods were available for stimulating the production of increased numbers of neutrophils and/or monocytes, and for enhancing their functional activity, then these methods should enhance resistance to infections.

It would be misrepresenting the situation to claim that these facts were uppermost in our minds during the 20-year period prior to the use of recombinant CSFs. There is an absence of any reference to such possible uses in our publications prior to 1986 and none of us can now recall whether such possibilities were so obvious that they scarcely warranted putting into print or whether the possibilities never occurred to us because, as cancer research workers, we had focused our clinical attention mainly on the problems of leukemia and, specifically, the myeloid leukemias.

Whatever the actual situation was at the time when CSFs were under test in vivo, we were not well placed to make any formal studies on responses in mice to experimental infections. None of us had experience with such models and our animal rooms were not designed for such work. It was other groups with suitable experience who were able, by using a variety of infections, to document that the use of CSFs in mice could enhance their resistance and survival following the injection of a variety of pathogenic organisms—much of the work being carried out in company laboratories.

The types of model used either involved the administration of cytotoxic drugs to damage the marrow and induce leukopenia—a model for cancer patients undergoing chemotherapy—or used neonatal or alcohol-pretreated models to mimic the situation in neonatal life or processes at work in some community-acquired infections. While the results provided clear evidence that G-CSF and GM-CSF could enhance resistance to a variety of pathogens, a particular pattern of responses and protection became evident. Injection of CSF prior to challenge with microorganisms could result in spectacularly enhanced resistance, whereas, if CSF treatment was delayed until after leukopenia had occurred and the microorganisms had been injected, enhanced resistance was much less evident and only became apparent when antibiotics were also used.

Time is of the essence in the effective suppression of an infection. Even a modest number of granulocytes and monocytes arriving early at a new site of infection will be much more effective in suppressing the infection than far larger numbers of cells arriving later.

While the cellular basis for the marked difference in the ability of the CSFs to enhance resistance to infections according to the timing of injections is not completely understood, experiments in our laboratory showed that to obtain a rapid adequate granulocytic response to a local infection, mature granulocytes need to be available in the marrow reserve for mobilization by chemotactic agents such as IL-8. Although both G-CSF and GM-CSF had been reported as being chemotactic in in vitro models, their local injection did not attract significant numbers of cells to the injection site. The role being played by CSFs was therefore first to ensure adequate numbers of mature cells had been formed in the marrow for recruitment by chemokines then, after arrival of these cells at an infection site, to ensure their most effective functional activity.

While we and others were able to document that sizable concentrations of CSF are produced in local sites of infection, these would not be able to prepare the body in advance by building up necessary reserves of mature cells. On this basis, preinjection of CSFs prior to infection would clearly be superior by being able to build up adequate numbers of mature cells. Clearly, if progenitor cell numbers had been depleted by chemotherapy or disease, the ability of CSFs to amplify the production of mature cells would be much reduced and likely to be slowed until more adequate numbers of progenitor cells had been built up.

These data on the use of CSFs in experimental infections had not been accumulated prior to the extensive clinical use of the CSFs. The pattern of current clinical use of the CSFs reflects to some degree the manner in which clinical usage generates its own traditions and habit patterns, uninfluenced by later more careful analyses of the basic biological events that occur during infections. Perhaps, with time, some of the present illogical methods will be modified.

I had vaguely supposed that there would be a considerable delay between the first in vivo experiments using CSFs in mice and their injection into humans. There would obviously be need for extensive toxicity studies in larger animals more suited for this purpose than mice, accompanied by an extended period of investigation of the effects of CSFs in primates.

The necessary toxicity studies were certainly performed in detail, at least in terms of short-term effects. Formal tests were not performed on

The new Walter and Eliza Hall Institute. We have occupied the left side of
the fifth floor since 1986.

the possible long-term consequences of a short course of CSF injections. As quasi-natural products, such a question is fairly illogical. No
one questions whether a short course of cortisone injections will have
any consequences after an interval of 20 years.

Equally illogical are tests on the actions of human CSFs in primates. There may well be short-term responses but there are species
differences from CSFs in primates, meaning that antibodies may well
develop to the injected human CSF, causing inactivation of the injected
CSF and a major distortion of the nature or magnitude of any responses
achievable. In the event, primate trials were carried out with each of the
human CSFs but these were not extensive—nor should they have been.

As a consequence there was to be a gap of less than two years
between the first studies on CSFs in mice and the first clinical trials.
After the long 20-year wait for the first murine trials, the impending in
vivo use of CSFs in patients was approaching at a rate that was slightly
discomforting.

A Parting of the Ways

The arrival on the scene of recombinant murine and human CSFs and the characterization of their biological actions in vitro and in vivo marked the close of another chapter of the CSF story. Thereafter, the story moves in four quite different directions sharing little in common—the clinical use of the CSFs, the search for CSF receptors, the role of the CSFs in leukemic transformation, and the generation of genetically modified animals lacking genes for the CSFs or their receptors. Our laboratories, with associated colleagues, were to be significantly involved in each of these separate endeavors, but, as they were largely unrelated one to another and were occurring simultaneously, it is not possible to recount developments in these four areas in a single consolidated description. Each will be described as a separate stream of investigations, but it needs to be kept in mind that they were in fact synchronous developments. To this degree, our group's activities often became fragmented into separate working groups, only coming together into combined teams when the needs of a particular study again required a multidisciplinary approach.

The completion of the studies on the responses of mice to injected recombinant CSF also marked a major change for our group. The entire Institute staff moved into a newly completed Hall Institute building. Our group had now a much larger set of laboratories and we seized this opportunity to recruit Nick Gough, David Gearing, and Tracy Willson to set up our own molecular biology laboratories. From this point onward, our group was to be able to use three disciplines—biology, biochemistry, and molecular biology—to tackle in a tightly integrated manner all future projects where such an approach seemed warranted.

TWELVE

The Clinical Use of the CSFs

The first clinical trial of recombinant CSF used GM-CSF and was a joint study in Boston and Los Angeles on AIDS patients, who are prone to low white cell counts from their disease and some of the agents used in their therapy. The results of this trial were published in 1987 by Jerome Groopman, David Golde, and colleagues. Although this is a complex disease situation, the injected GM-CSF was able to elicit dose-dependent increases in neutrophils, monocytes, and eosinophils without more than mild side effects.

Most of the preliminary clinical trials on G-CSF and GM-CSF were carried out reasonably synchronously in 1988 and 1989 and involved clinical groups in the United States, Japan, Europe, and in Melbourne, Australia, under the direction of George Morstyn and Richard Fox. For the most part, these studies were performed on patients with various types of cancer or lymphoma. This choice of patients was based on the more ready availability of cancer patients as in-patients with well-defined disease states. More importantly, because such patients are likely to receive chemotherapy, they constitute by far the largest group of patients who might suffer bone marrow damage and consequent low white cell levels that might be in need of attempted stimulation using CSFs.

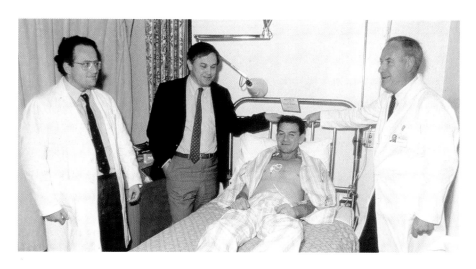

George Morstyn, Richard Fox, and Don Metcalf with the first Australian patient to receive G-CSF.

In dose escalation studies to define the dosages causing unacceptable toxicity, it became evident that G-CSF injections induced few serious side effects other than some bone pain over marrow-bearing bones. GM-CSF, on first injection into some patients, caused transient hypoxic responses but not with subsequent injections. GM-CSF in effective doses did cause some aches and pains that were not of serious clinical concern, but, if higher GM-CSF doses were used, symptoms consistent with inflammatory responses in muscle, pericardium, and joints sometimes resulted. These defined limits of dose usage for GM-CSF and were likely to have been the consequence of macrophage activation by GM-CSF, leading to the production of toxic macrophage-derived products such as γ-interferon, TNF, or IL-1. Restriction of doses to levels that were still clearly active on hematopoietic cells has resulted in both agents normally being able to be used without causing side effects of concern.

As had been the case in mice, G-CSF was able to elicit higher granulocyte responses in the blood than GM-CSF at comparable doses, although the responses to GM-CSF could also include increases in monocytes and eosinophils. Subcutaneous injections were found to be the most satisfactory, and elevated white cell levels could be sustained for as long as injections were continued, without any dimunition of the response or decreases in red cell or platelet levels.

These phase I trials were followed in Melbourne and other centers by trials in which the effectiveness of CSFs was established in achieving useful clinical outcomes. Again the patient groups used were cancer or lymphoma patients receiving chemotherapy or similar patients receiving more intensive therapy requiring the administration of life-saving marrow transplants. The questions at issue were whether the CSFs could significantly shorten the period before granulocytes recovered to levels enhancing protection against infections (greater than 1,000/μl), whether the CSFs could reduce the frequency of infections or the use of antibiotics in such patients, whether this might decrease mortality, and, finally, whether CSF use was cost-effective in terms of reducing hospitalization times and overall treatment costs.

These phase II and III trials on slightly different patient groups were run in many centers in Australia, the United States, Japan, and Europe and, despite the heterogeneity of patients involved, the results were surprisingly uniform. Periods of post-treatment neutropenia could be reduced by intervals typically of 7 to 10 days. Fever in these patients can indicate infections but often is not able to be associated with an obvious infection.

The prophylactic use of CSFs following chemotherapy was found to reduce the occurrence, severity, and duration of neutropenia and the occurrence of fever, allowing many patients to avoid hospitalization because of these complications. For those patients becoming hospitalized, benefits of CSF treatment in terms of reduced certified infections, reduced antibiotic use, and reduced duration of hospitalization were able to be documented, even if the benefits were sometimes of modest dimensions.

The use of CSFs following chemotherapy did appear to be a valuable contribution to the management and well-being of these patients and in most centers was assessed as being cost-effective. On this basis, successful applications were lodged in various countries to have G-CSF or GM-CSF licensed for certain defined clinical uses.

At present, the most common forms of cancer in which CSF treatment is used are breast cancer, non-Hodgkin's lymphoma, and certain types of lung cancer and leukemia. As is often the case in medicine, where a therapy is used prophylacticaly, not all patients are necessarily going to benefit, but until methods are developed for identifying those who will from those who will not, there is little option but to administer such therapy to most.

There were, however, some obvious examples where CSF treatment was highly effective and at times life saving. There are two uncommon genetic diseases in which sustained or recurrent failure of neutrophil production occurs—congenital neutropenia and cyclic neutropenia. Cyclic neutropenic patients suffer recurrent decreases in neutrophil levels with episodes of minor or major infection on an approximate 21-day cycle and use of either G-CSF or GM-CSF administered daily clearly reduced the occurrence of such infections. CSF treatment did not actually prevent the swings in neutrophil levels, merely elevated the nadirs between peaks to levels above 1,000/µl. In young children with congenital neutropenia, matters are much more desperate with the continuous occurrence of complex, life-threatening infections. GM-CSF appeared not to be effective in such patients but high doses of G-CSF were.

Patients of both types have now been on continuous daily CSF treatment for more than a decade without loss of effectiveness of the agents, the only downside being the requirement for daily injections. This situation is no worse than that for insulin-dependent diabetics but, nonetheless, is in need of improvement by the development of slow-release formulations, modified CSFs with a longer half-life, or orally administered small molecular weight analogues, all of which should be able to be developed.

One disturbing occurrence in some patients with congenital neutropenia has been the subsequent development of acute myeloid leukemia. For reasons to be discussed later, this is almost certainly not due to some leukemogenic action of G-CSF. Rather, some of these patients were actually in a preleukemic state, a fact that, prior to G-CSF therapy, had not been recognizable because of their early death from infections. By preventing death from infections, the true nature of their disease was revealed.

Another group of patients where CSF treatment had more tangible effects was transplant patients, often with infections, in whom

Ashley Dunn and Nick Gough, the cloners of GM-CSF with Jose Carreras, an early recipient.

regeneration of the marrow had failed to occur or was proceeding abnormally slowly. In such patients CSF treatment was often able to promote the regeneration of the grafted cells and eliminate the infections. A somewhat similar situation exists with patients over the age of 60 where chemotherapy-induced marrow damage can cause severe problems. In such patients CSF treatment can be of definite assistance.

Given that CSF treatment is almost universally commenced after chemotherapy and consequent neutropenia, the clinical responses to CSFs have been in line with what the various experimental models of infection later documented. This administration of CSF *after* chemotherapy is suboptimal; responses are slow and the advantages still require the use of antibiotics to become apparent. Furthermore, only a few patients have ever been administered combined CSF therapy despite the well-based in vitro studies showing the superiority of this usage of CSFs. This appears to be the consequence of the CSFs being products of different companies. Because of this no costly formal trials have ever been performed, for example, combining G-CSF and

GM-CSF, and so no licensing has occurred for their combined use. It is also frustrating to record that clinical trials of the CSFs in infections unrelated to cancer therapy have not been extensive and, again, the combined use of CSFs has never been tested. For laboratory workers, this is a somewhat bizarre situation that is proving difficult to resolve from outside the clinical arena.

After the clinical usage of the CSFs had fallen into a defined pattern, newer developments in the laboratory began to indicate that GM-CSF has some unusual additional biological actions. GM-CSF has proved to be necessary for the development of functionally active dendritic cells. Dendritic cells of this type are mainly the progeny of macrophage precursors and have the special function of taking up foreign antigens, breaking these into small peptide subunits, and then presenting these on the dendritic cell membrane to adjacent T lymphocytes. This is the key process by which T lymphocyte activation occurs, leading either to T lymphocyte-mediated processes such as killing of virally infected or tumor cells or to activation by T lymphocytes of B lymphocytes to produce antibody. GM-CSF is therefore a key regulator in many types of immune response and is of particular importance where the antigen concerned is weak, such as with hepatitis B antigen, Calmette-Guérin bacillus (BCG), or tumor antigens.

Although there have been pilot clinical trials demonstrating the effectiveness of GM-CSF in this adjuvant role in enhancing immune responses to weak antigens, the companies involved have not carried these observations forward to achieve widespread clinical use of GM-CSF as a useful adjunct in immunization.

A somewhat similar situation exists with the local use of GM-CSF to accelerate the healing of chronic ulcers or infected wounds. Here the mechanism involved is unclear—whether local activation of macrophages or dendritic cells or a possible capacity of GM-CSF to enhance skin epithelial cell proliferation. Pilot studies have reported remarkable results with the use of GM-CSF, but again there have been no formal documented trials that could lead to licensing and thus no extension of these applications to conventional clinical practice.

These episodes identify a deficiency in our current methods for regulating the introduction of new drugs to the clinic. How does one act when faced with recalcitrant companies unable or unmotivated to carry out the necessary clinical trials for a purpose that may be very useful for individual patients but may not necessarily be a highly profitable use? Fully documented and expensive clinical trials are currently needed for official approval and licensing, but if these are not attempted is there a way out of an unsatisfactory impasse? In my view, a sensible and ethical solution must be found because the present situation is quite indefensible.

Clinical trials of IL-3 (Multi-CSF) began in the United States and Europe in 1989 with the usual dose-escalation studies. Because of the known actions of IL-3 in vitro on multiple lineages of hematopoietic cells, the hope was that its use might provide an added dimension to the emerging ability of G-CSF and GM-CSF to stimulate granulocyte and/or monocyte populations. In particular, it was hoped that IL-3 would promote the formation of red cells and platelets in addition to any actions it might have on granulocyte-macrophage populations.

Attention was concentrated therefore on certain disease states, such as the myelodysplastic states, where there is multilineage failure of blood cell formation, in addition to the usual cancer patients receiving myelotoxic chemotherapy.

IL-3 proved to be reasonably well tolerated although sometimes causing low fever, flu-like symptoms, and headache. Some improvement of granulocyte and macrophage levels was observed in various clinical situations with, on occasion, some improvement in platelet levels, but actions on platelets and erythroid cells were neither major nor consistent, an outcome that was in line with experience in mice.

IL-3 had been noted in in vitro experiments to stimulate the proliferation of some more ancestral cells than the other CSFs and the notion had been raised that it was classifiable as an early acting regulator. If this were so, it might be useful clinically to administer IL-3 before agents like GM-CSF or G-CSF because the latter agents might then have more target cells on which to act. Some primate and clinical trials did suggest that the sequential use of IL-3 followed by GM-CSF or G-CSF did enhance resulting cellular responses but such enhancement was not particularly dramatic.

While the use of IL-3 did seem to permit the delivery of more intensive chemotherapy regimens, clinical trials of IL-3 have tended to diminish in the past five years. Several factors have possibly contributed to this decline in the fortunes of IL-3. It had not proved to have strong multilineage actions and its actions on granulocytes and monocytes were no stronger than those of G-CSF or GM-CSF already in extensive clinical use. In addition, in some patients a reaction resembling hypersensitivity occurred, possibly as a consequence of mast cell activation. These considerations, when combined, do not provide a particularly favorable situation for completing expensive clinical trials and IL-3 may continue to languish unless some particular disease situation is found to exhibit unusually favorable responses to IL-3.

Clinical trials of M-CSF had an unusual beginning with trials in Japan of native M-CSF purified from human urine. This agent unexpectedly promoted some increases in granulocyte levels, possibly indirectly by inducing rises in G-CSF or GM-CSF. Publication of the first clinical trials of recombinant M-CSF began in 1991 and, fairly uniformly, M-CSF was noted to induce modest increases in monocyte levels that were often accompanied by a transient decrease in platelet levels, possibly the consequence of accelerated platelet destruction by activated monocytes and macrophages. More intriguingly, the use of M-CSF in transplant patients with acquired fungal infections did seem to be of value in controlling these infections, again presumably because of macrophage activation. Several groups also obtained suggestive evidence that M-CSF might enhance host antitumor responses, again presumably macrophage mediated.

Again, as in the case of IL-3, further clinical exploitation of M-CSF seems to have stalled in the past five years. This may have been because of concerns regarding falling platelet levels associated with its use and also because its apparent action in elevating monocyte levels was no stronger than achievable using the more established agent, GM-CSF.

It is at this point that the limitations of transferring potentially useful agents from the laboratory to the clinic become apparent. For valid enough commercial reasons, a company is reluctant to try to introduce a new agent into clinical use if its apparent actions are no stronger than existing agents. Indeed, regulatory authorities would regard such approaches with skepticism. More importantly, there are severe limitations to what is observable or measurable in a patient compared with a mouse. Monitoring of hematopoietic responses in humans is essentially limited to blood cell parameters and occasional marrow samples. If, as was the case for G-CSF, peripheral blood changes are readily detectable, there is no problem documenting the occurrence of responses. If, however, responses occur but are in nonaccessible tissues, the agent may well fare badly in conventional assessment. This is almost certainly the situation with GM-CSF and M-CSF. As we shall see later, for example, M-CSF has profound actions that are probably unique on macrophage populations in various tissues. These have little hope of being demonstrable in conventional clinical trials and the possibly important aspects and virtues of an agent like M-CSF will be overlooked.

One can only hope that these initial trials do not close the book finally on the possible clinical value of agents like IL-3 and M-CSF. We are still in the early phases of clinical use of these agents. There is a reason why these agents exist and there must therefore be certain clinical situations where their use will be important.

Peripheral Blood Stem Cells

During our investigations on the first patients injected with G-CSF, we were determined to document as fully as possible all changes occurring in the patients. This required tight coordination between clinical and nursing staff in the Royal Melbourne Hospital and laboratory staff in our adjacent Hall Institute laboratories. This teamwork ran very smoothly. One thing we had agreed to do was to subject blood samples and the occasional available marrow samples to careful analysis using semisolid cultures. These studies were primarily in the hands of an able German postdoc, Uli Dührsen, with several of us assisting when required. The results of this analysis were unexpected and were to render the technique of bone marrow transplantation essentially obsolete.

What was observed was that, after five or six days of CSF injections, progenitor cell levels in the blood rose about 100-fold to attain the same levels as present in the bone marrow. This dramatic rise should not have been entirely unexpected. Essentially this experiment had been performed in mice by Ray Bradley 20 years earlier, admittedly using unpurified CSF. However, he too found a major increase in colony-forming cells in the blood and recorded these observations. In the subsequent 20 years we had simply forgotten these results.

Our observations were quickly confirmed by other clinical groups and, in clinical trials with GM-CSF, we and others observed similar elevations of progenitor cells, although not as high as those achievable by G-CSF.

What was being monitored were changes in progenitor cell numbers. Progenitor cells were known not to be capable of repopulating a marrow-depleted animal but it seemed likely that parallel changes would be occurring in the levels of stem cells of a type that would be able to sustain long-term hematopoiesis.

Peripheral blood had acquired a bad reputation from early studies in mice and dogs where such cells had seemed unable to generate hematopoietic populations that could be sustained on a long-term basis. Despite this, later studies by Richman had noted that chemotherapy itself can increase colony-forming cell levels in the blood and studies by Gianni and colleagues in Italy demonstrated that blood taken from patients after chemotherapy was effective as a transplantated population.

Beginning in 1989, Bill Sheridan, Chris Juttner, and transplantation colleagues in Melbourne and Adelaide made the decision to attempt to use what came to be called peripheral blood stem cells (PBSC) that had been mobilized into the blood by G-CSF injections. They did play it safe with the first group of patients by supplementing the PBSC with marrow cells in case PBSC were in fact hopeless as repopulating cells. CSF injections with subsequent harvesting of PBSC by apheresis were carried out mainly with lymphoma patients prior to chemotherapy and the cells were stored for reinfusion after chemotherapy had produced marrow damage. These clinical studies proceeded smoothly and the hope was that the double population, with CSF treatment posttransplantation, would achieve restoration of neutrophil levels in the blood more rapidly than experience had shown marrow cells able to do. The results were very satisfactory in that the combined transplant allowed rapid regeneration of white cell numbers. Indeed, it was found subsequently that in many patients pretreated with CSF to mobilize PBSC no further acceleration of regeneration is achievable by the administration of CSFs after the PBSC have been administered.

After intensive chemotherapy, two clinical problems can result—very low white cell numbers, requiring the use of special nursing and protected wards to minimize the risk of serious infections, and also low numbers of platelets that are required for blood clotting. The latter problem can require the expensive transfusion of platelets and is often the main cause for the transplant patients spending prolonged periods in hospital. An extraordinary outcome of the use of PBSC was that recovery of blood platelet levels was also markedly accelerated, reducing the need for platelet transfusions and extended hospitalization.

With the initial success of the combined transplantation, quite quickly the collection of bone marrow cells was able to be abandoned and equally good responses were obtained with transplants of peripheral blood stem cells alone.

As a consequence of this twin outcome from the use of PBSC, within a decade the occasions on which marrow transplants are performed have fallen dramatically and for most patients this latter technique is now obsolete or quite inferior. For many less intensively pretreated transplant patients the entire transplant procedure can be performed on an outpatient basis and no hospitalization is required—a remarkable transformation of clinical medicine to arise almost as a side consequence of the clinical introduction of CSFs.

This maneuver of mobilizing PBSC with G-CSF before cancer chemotherapy is commenced was carefully quantified by Glenn Begley and has become a relatively simple procedure in which the patient self-injects G-CSF at home then comes to an outpatient center where the blood cells are collected much as a patient would make a blood donation. The apheresis machine collecting the blood actually separates the white blood cell fractions that also contain the PBSC from the red cells, which are then returned to the patient, leaving the patient in no way anemic from the procedure. The plastic collecting bags are then stored at $-70°$ in liquid nitrogen, the best method for keeping the cells alive and fully functional.

In different centers slightly varying procedures are used, such as combining some chemotherapy with G-CSF treatment to increase cell harvests, but the common goal is to make use of the the superior properties of PBSC.

This is one of those uncommon situations where clinical studies generated data that were initially more extensive than those existing at the time from experimental animals. However, it was quickly established that mice respond to CSF injections in the same manner as humans and this has allowed the phenomenon to be analyzed in more detail. At first it was supposed that, after CSF treatment, the number of megakaryocyte progenitors (the source of platelets) might rise to exceptionally high levels in the blood as the basis of the dramatic acceleration of platelet recovery. However, this was not observed in our original studies on patients injected with G-CSF and also proved not to be the case from our studies in mice. The murine studies allowed stem cells to be assayed separately and, as suspected, stem cell levels do rise in parallel with progenitor cell levels and these stem cells initiate the accelerated repopulation.

The complex mechanisms by which G-CSF induces release of these cells from the marrow to the blood are still not fully explained nor is the reason why PBSC are so superior to marrow transplants. However, a major reason for the superiority of PBSC may be fairly simple—it is possible to harvest far more cells from the peripheral blood than in the average collection of bone marrow cells. It is likely that the better performance of PBSC is simply a matter of numbers of cells available for reinfusion. There are differences between patients in how many PBSC can be harvested and comparable differences have been observed by us between different mouse strains. Mobilization is therefore influenced by certain genes and the mapping of these genes with their identification is still in progress.

A somewhat similar clinical use of the CSFs is to stimulate the development in volunteers of high levels of mature neutrophils in the blood, which can then be collected. These can be reinfused into patients during the initial phases after chemotherapy when white cell levels are very low, helping maintain neutrophil levels during that critical early phase when the patients are most at risk of acquiring infections.

The past decade of clinical use of the CSFs has produced a rather mixed outcome—dramatic changes in transplantation medicine, moderate success in helping manage cancer patients following chemotherapy, and some, but not uniformly satisfactory, results in the management of infections. All of these are outcomes from treatment procedures that are known from basic studies to be suboptimal either because of suboptimal timing of treatment or from failure to use combinations with other CSFs or hematopoietic regulators.

A decade may seem a long time in clinical medicine but my view is that these are still early days in the clinical use of CSFs and much better results should be achievable eventually. It almost goes without saying that pharmaceutical companies could be very helpful in accelerating this progress and minimizing discomfort to patients by developing modified versions of the CSFs that result in an extended half life in serum, slow-release formulations, or orally administrable low molecular analogues to minimize the present need for injections during treatment.

Predictions are a hazardous business in medical science, but if I had to give my opinion on the disease states in which the future clinical use of the CSFs will prove to be most effective it would be in the area of infections. We are approaching an era where antibiotics are becoming less and less effective. If this becomes more apparent, the only obvious recourse is to strengthen host resistance—either specific or nonspecific. The ability of GM-CSF to act as a powerful adjuvant in enhancing immune responses, for example, to the tubercle bacillus, must be exploited as must the ability of the CSFs alone or in combination to enhance the actions of granulocytes and macrophages, preferably early in infections or in situations where infections are likely to occur and be life threatening. The agents are available; what is needed is the determination to securely document the situations and manner in which their use will be most beneficial.

THIRTEEN

The Cloning and Characterization of Receptors for the CSFs and Other Regulators

It comes as a surprise to younger colleagues when it is pointed out to them that, during the initial work on CSFs, nothing was known for certain about how proteins of this type actually interact with their responding cells. How did the hematopoietic regulator molecules recognize, bind to, then interact with their appropriate responding cells? Were they then pinocytosed or somehow engulfed by the cells? And what happened next? Did the CSF molecules themselves go to the nucleus to influence the various genes whose function needed to be altered? Our early papers on CSFs occasionally contained such speculations and, when now read, arouse mild amusement until it is recognized that these papers were written prior to the discovery of specific membrane receptors for proteins.

That proteins could bind to cell membranes and that this binding appeared to be specific was slowly documented in the 1970s. Acceptance of these observations was slow and somewhat grudging until more precise measurements such as Scatchard analyses were developed. The actual nature of these membrane receptors remained unclear until the landmark cloning in 1984 of a cDNA encoding the membrane receptor for epidermal growth factor. By this time, all four of the CSFs had been purified and work on the CSFs had been in progress for more than 15 years. Little wonder that the early CSF papers were so vague on how the CSFs might actually act on responding cells!

As cDNAs for further receptors were isolated, it became reasonable to assume that hematopoietic cells were expressing on their membrane comparable specific receptors for the various CSFs.

Indeed, when the CSFs were purified and could be radiolabeled, we were able to document the presence of these receptors on various blood cells and also the surprisingly low numbers of such receptors on individual cells.

The documentation of the likely presence of receptors for the CSFs by autoradiography of cells binding radiolabeled CSF was occurring in our laboratory from 1978 to 1985—the same period during which the polyfunctionality of the CSFs was becoming increasingly inescapable. This immediately began to raise problems. For each CSF, only a single type of receptor seemed to exist. If this was so, how could a CSF-receptor complex initiate such different responses within the cell—responses that had to occur in widely differing locations and involve a variety of genes? Resolution of this puzzle was going to require that the receptors be characterized at the level of amino acid sequence and ultimately at the three-dimensional level.

Purification of the few hundred CSF receptors present on the surface of most hematopoietic cells seemed hopeless to contemplate. The project clearly needed the introduction of molecular biology to clone cDNAs encoding these glycoproteins whose size was even larger than that of the CSFs themselves.

The first characterization of a CSF receptor by Charles Sherr and colleagues in 1985 was dramatic and unexpected. It arose from perceptive consideration of the likely transmembrane nature of the product of the viral oncogene, v-fms, its distribution on various cells, and the general similarity of this protein to the emerging properties of the membrane receptor for M-CSF. Antisera to v-fms were able to precipitate membrane-derived M-CSF receptors. This raised the possibility that the oncogenic virus may have acquired from some host cell what amounted to the gene encoding the receptor for M-CSF. When the corresponding normal mouse cDNA (c-fms) was isolated by Rothwell and Rohrschneider in 1987, transfection of this cDNA to suitable target cells made it evident that high-affinity M-CSF receptors were now being expressed on the cell membranes.

A minimum of two glycoprotein chains is required to form a high-affinity receptor for these types of regulator molecules. In some cases, the two chains are identical (homodimers) and in other cases they are dissimilar (heterodimers). The v-fms and c-fms experiments were easier than they might have been because the M-CSF receptor happens to be a homodimer. The M-CSF receptor proved to have a cytoplasmic tyrosine kinase domain that became activated by cross-phosphorylation when binding by M-CSF brought two receptor chains into apposition. In this it was similar to the prototype epidermal growth factor receptor that had been the subject of recent intensive study.

This was a highly satisfactory initial outcome. A CSF receptor had been cloned and characterized with minimal effort and, furthermore, the structure of this receptor was similar to the prototype receptor for epidermal growth factor. There was some expectation that the other CSF receptors might well be somewhat similar homodimers with familiar cytoplasmic domains able to initiate signaling.

Events were to prove that the M-CSF receptor is not typical of receptors for most hematopoietic growth factors. A few are indeed homodimers but only three contain tyrosine kinase domains in their cytoplasmic regions.

In 1988, Nick Nicola, with David Gearing and Nick Gough from our new molecular biology laboratories, began to address seriously the problem of how a cDNA for the GM-CSF receptor might be cloned. With his background expertise in radiolabeling and autoradiography, Nick Nicola opted for an expression cloning approach and chose the human GM-CSF receptor as his target for cloning. Human placental tissue had been shown by him to bind ^{125}I-labeled human GM-CSF, so presumably there were cells in this tissue expressing receptors for GM-CSF. mRNA was extracted from human placental tissue, a cDNA library was constructed, and cDNA pools from this library were used to transfect monkey COS cells, not expressing receptors, growing as monolayers in flat-bottomed flasks. ^{125}I-GM-CSF was then added to the flasks and, after a suitable incubation period, the bottom of the flask with its monolayer of cells was detached and coated with photographic

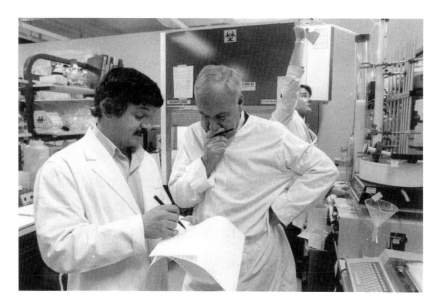

Nick Nicola and Don Metcalf pondering over the latest receptor binding data (Bill McKinstry in background).

emulsion. The hope was that one or more of the cells in such mono-layers might now be expressing GM-CSF receptors and, if so, might have bound sufficient ^{125}I-GM-CSF to be revealed by autoradiography. Although the procedure is tedious, it worked well. A placental cDNA pool was identified that could reproducibly induce some cells to be radioactively labeled and, by progressively splitting this pool of cDNAs, a clone was isolated that was highly active in inducing COS cells to bind ^{125}I-GM-CSF. This project had succeeded by 1989 in isolating a cDNA clone encoding a specific, but low-affinity, GM-CSF receptor. Receptors only become of high affinity if both chains are coexpressed, so the technique was fortunate in being able to identify a cDNA encoding only the low-affinity specific GM-CSFα receptor chain.

This autoradiographic expression screening method was to be used subsequently by others to clone specific receptors for other regulators and clearly had the ability to achieve the difficult feat of cloning low-affinity receptors.

We found that insertion of the low-affinity human α-chain receptors for GM-CSF into murine FDC-P1 cells was successful in now allowing these cells to be stimulated to proliferate by human GM-CSF. Although we were not in a position to recognize it at the time, this successful response hinged on use of a mouse cell line that was already expressing the murine GM-CSF receptor β-chain and on the ability of these α- and β-chains from different species to interact well enough to deliver a mitotic signal to the cells, even if rather high concentrations of human GM-CSF were required.

When we described our cloning of the α-chain of the human GM-CSF receptor, we pointed out that there were certain similarities in its structure to those of the recently cloned receptors for IL-6, erythropoietin, IL-2, and prolactin. In particular, there was a common WSXWS motif near the transmembrane region and spaced cysteine residues in the extracellular domain. We suggested that these common regions might define a new class of receptors and this has subsequently proved to be the case, with a majority of the hemopoietic regulator receptors containing what has become referred to as the WSXWS box and cysteine-containing hemopoietin domains.

Events then moved very quickly in the hands of Akito Miyajima and his colleagues at DNAX and Linda Park and her colleagues at Immunex. In a very short time cDNAs were isolated for the α-chain of human and murine IL-3 receptors and for the murine GM-CSF receptor. More importantly, the key β-receptor chains for these specific α-chains were identified and cloned. These were necessary to interact with the α-chains in the presence of the CSF to generate an activated signaling complex. These discoveries revealed a novel situation in that, on human cells, the same β-chain partnered the α-chains for GM-CSF, IL-3, and IL-5. In the mouse, the situation was more complex in that there were two β-chains that could interact with the IL-3 α-chain, a β-common chain as for human cells but also a private β-chain interacting only with IL-3. The existence of common β-receptor chains was the physical explanation for the competition we had documented years earlier between the binding of GM-CSF and IL-3 on marrow cells when the β-chains were present in limiting numbers and were being competed for by the two types of α-chain. We were later to find that in the mouse, the IL-3 α-chain preferentially uses the private IL-3-specific β-chain, which forms complexes of higher affinity and efficiency than those formed using β-common chains.

None of the receptor chains for GM-CSF and IL-3 contained tyrosine kinase domains so a major problem was arising as to how such chains might initiate any sort of signaling following binding of the CSF.

While this complexity was being unraveled by our U.S. colleagues, we set out to clone a cDNA for the G-CSF receptor, again using the autoradiographic expression screening method, although it proved a troublesome project with many false positive cells because of the highly sticky nature of G-CSF. For the second time a G-CSF project of ours was aborted by the success of the Nagata group in Tokyo. They seemed to be our private nemesis. In a bizarre repeat of the earlier G-CSF manuscript episode, I was sent for refereeing their manuscript describing the successful cloning of the G-CSF receptor! What could we do but again graciously accept defeat and applaud a fine piece of work. As before, I did as much as a referee can do to ensure that the manuscript was accepted for publication.

The G-CSF receptor was another homodimer, again not containing tyrosine kinase domains, although it did contain the WSXWS and hemopoietin domains characteristic of receptors in this new class.

Following the identification of the M-CSF receptor, the cloning of the remaining CSF receptors only occupied a period of four years. These discoveries were to provide key systems for beginning the long task, still in progress, of dissecting the substructure of these receptors and determining how signaling is initiated, particularly by the nontyrosine kinase receptors.

After being soundly beaten in our race to clone the G-CSF receptor, we commenced in 1990 a major effort to clone a cDNA for the receptor for leukemia inhibitory factor (LIF). LIF was a molecule in which we had developed a strong interest, having recently purified and cloned this regulator (see Chapter 14). Again, we used Nick Nicola's screening strategy to search for transfected cells now expressing the LIF receptor and thereby acquiring the ability to bind radiolabeled LIF. We again also used human placental cDNA libraries because of the known presence of the LIF receptor in placental tissue. This proved to be the beginning of a very labor intensive and frustrating two-year period of complete failure. We had some concern that our placental cDNA library might not be adequate for the purpose because most of the cDNAs in it were of relatively small size and might not have included a LIF receptor cDNA if the receptor was a large molecule (as turned out to be the case). We did make further libraries with a better representation of larger inserts to overcome what we feared might be a major problem. Radiolabeled LIF also turned out to be a fairly nasty material to use with autoradiography because it often contained aggregates of radioactive material that produced cell-like artifacts in our cell preparations. These were vexatious enough problems when coupled with seemingly endless six-hour days of microscopy on unstained monolayers, looking unsuccessfully for a single positive cell. In all, I spent a year in this soul-destroying labor with, at the end, no positive result and not a word of publishable information. This had never happened to me before and I sincerely hope it never happens again. Expression screening can be spectacularly successful but it can be an equally devastating waste of time and effort.

What we did not realize was that the whole project was doomed from the outset. We were, of course, using human LIF as the radiolabeled ligand because we knew that murine LIF has no action on human cells and does not bind to the human LIF receptor. What we did not know was that the human LIF cDNA we were using to produce recombinant human LIF was no such thing. It was a murine LIF cDNA that had been mislabeled when stored in our cDNA bank. The assays used to monitor the production and purification of LIF involve murine cells, which respond equally to human or murine LIF. Short of sequencing the cDNA, there was no way to distinguish between the two with the bioassays in use and there had never seemed a reason to resequence the purported human LIF cDNA. We were not able to establish how the ampoules came to be mislabeled but have our own views on this question. Suffice it to say that we did not succeed in cloning the human LIF receptor.

This pursuit of hematopoietic regulator receptors was an exciting-enough endeavor because such receptors were clearly necessary tools to enable studies on the substructure of receptors that initiated the various actions of the regulators. However, I was beginning to have some serious misgivings about our program. We were no longer highly focused on the characterization of the CSFs and their receptors. LIF had come on board as a molecule of major, but complex, importance for our group and we were beginning to be stretched in our ability to perform in-depth studies.

Life within our group was about to become much more complex and fragmented. We had survived the birth and development of the Ludwig Institute from our Unit but were now to be confronted with a more dislocating creation. Our federal government had decided to fund combined research-industrial consortia (CRC), which were demonstrably capable of excellent basic research but with projects that would benefit from the combination of a number of scientific subdisciplines with industrial assistance. This required the coordination of a number of groups from physically separate research institutes together with an industrial partner who could fast-track suitable discoveries and begin their commercialization. This program of cooperative research centers has in general been successful both scientifically and commercially, but it did introduce, as it was intended to, a commitment to have specific products in the forefront of attention. This variant of the academic versus cloning company models attempts to keep the good aspects of academic science but provide them, when appropriate, with a certain industrial clout.

We had prepared a submission for such a cooperative research center based on cellular growth factors and were successful in being selected as one of the initial CRCs funded. This had a number of consequences, both foreseen and unforeseen. We essentially lost Nick Nicola as an active bench scientist because he became director of this CRC, with the taxing job of trying to coordinate programs developed in four research institutes and an embryo pharmaceutical company. The advantages balancing this serious loss were substantially increased staff numbers and operating funds. There were also now many additional people squeezed into our existing laboratory space.

I believe that research groups probably have an ideal size of around 30, but our combined groups now exceeded this number, and we were no longer working in our normal ratio of about one scientist to one technical assistant. It began to be difficult to ensure that all technical assistants were working under effective supervision and with a good knowledge of what every other Unit member was doing. Worse was the expanded range of scientific subjects being tackled or requiring collaborative work, because sometimes this work was not central to the existing projects of individual scientists. The dilution of effort and lack of focus rapidly became evident, if for no other reason than it seemed to require almost continuous meetings to keep each other cross-informed. Extra resources and money also required the creation of new projects based on existing technology, with further dilution of focused effort.

This became very apparent with our work on hematopoietic receptors. A program was developed by Doug Hilton based on the presumption that additional hematopoietic receptors could be discovered by making use of the common WSXWS motif of already known receptors. Redundant probes based on this sequence might well be able to discover new members of this family of receptors. This was a correct prediction, but the real hope behind the program was that, given a novel receptor, this could be used to detect and purify novel hematopoietic growth factors either by physical methods or by inserting the receptor into suitable cells that could serve as bioassays for the presumed new growth factor. A novel variant of this technique would be to try to transform receptor-bearing cells to autonomous cells, based on an acquired autocrine ability to produce the growth factor being sought. In a model system using FDC-P1 cells with inserted erythropoietin receptors, John Rasko was indeed able to isolate autonomous clones now producing erythropoietin, which validated the general approach.

In an unkind twist of fate, we spent much time trying to develop autonomous FDC-P1 cells expressing the inserted mpl receptor, likely to be the receptor for the long-sought regulator of platelet production, thrombopoietin. Despite much effort, we failed, merely discovering autonomous FDC-P1 lines producing either GM-CSF or Multi-CSF— the two regulators able to support the survival and proliferation of FDC-P1 cells. A competing group in Seattle was successful in this same approach with much less effort and obtained transformed cells producing thrombopoietin. Again, we could only accept our defeat with as much grace as possible. One cannot always expect to win when many are active in the field and there is rarely something absolutely unique about a good idea.

We became enmeshed then in a global search for receptors with WSXWS motifs to provide specific traps for discovering what were

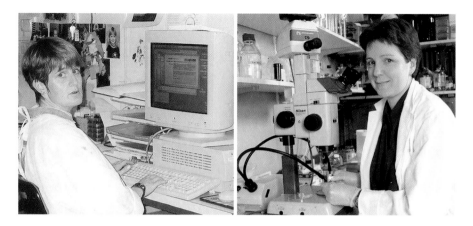

Tracy Willson (left), receptor cloner, and Lorraine Robb (right), receptor inactivator.

generally agreed to be undiscovered hematopoietic regulators. This approach, under the leadership of Tracy Willson, was literally a fishing expedition and in the period from 1993 to 1996 we discovered a number of candidate receptors. The first three isolated were indeed novel transmembrane proteins with an appropriate structure for receptors—most likely α-receptor chains because of their small intracytoplasmic tails. Regrettably, a lot of effort in each case established that these were the receptors for known regulators—IL-11, IL-13, and leptin. From the simple viewpoint of discovering something novel, each project had been successful enough but the approach had failed to provide the hoped-for lock for a novel regulator key. Equally seriously, the receptors concerned were for agents in whose biology we had no expertise and little incentive to be latecomers in well-established areas of biology. We wisely chose to cut our losses with IL-13 and leptin and not to proceed further.

The discovery of the IL-11 receptor (also sharing a common gp130 signaling chain with the LIF and IL-6 receptors) prompted Glenn Begley and Lorraine Robb in our group to spend much effort to establish the hematological actions of IL-11 and the consequences of inactivation of the IL-11 receptor. The hematological consequences of this inactivation were minimal and the action of IL-11 in stimulating platelet formation was already being strongly pursued by other groups. What inactivation of the IL-11 receptor gene did result in was mice with a dramatic failure of placental development during pregnancy. Although this was a striking finding, we were not an obstetric unit nor a general developmental biology group and it became arguable whether we should divert a sizable fraction of our resources into these areas.

A further unknown receptor, NR6, was uncovered in this program, and this proved to be a particularly difficult problem because the cDNA concerned encoded merely a soluble molecule with receptor characteristics. We were never able to uncover a longer transmembrane version of this cDNA. A search for an NR6 binding protein by physical methods was unsuccessful and in desperation an NR6 knockout mouse was developed. This mouse died within 24 hours of birth with minimal hematopoietic abnormalities and no detectable organ pathology but an inability to suckle. From the viewpoint of discovering a novel ligand, this project so far has also been unsuccessful.

By this time, members of our groups were also engaged in studies on mpl, LIF, and IL-6 receptors. While information of quality was being established about the structure of these receptors, matters had almost reached the stage of one person per receptor, with little of the work adding qualitatively new information to notions of receptor action. The results were merely extending slightly information already being gathered by other groups.

We had in essence fallen prey to the temptation of big science—tackling far too many disparate projects, often effectively enough, by recruiting additional pairs of hands when the need arose, but not generating discoveries that were being developed in depth and with potential commercial applications. The additional demands of the CRC with its special objectives was, on balance, rendering our work less creative. That we had cloned a number of missing receptors was certainly an accomplishment, but the work was fragmented, dealt with widely differing biological systems, and was not allowing anyone, senior or junior, to build a growing reputation as *the* expert on a particular subject. It was also evident that this receptor-first approach had not succeeded in uncovering any new hematopoietic regulators—the original objective of the approach.

Without any sort of formal decision being reached, this search for new receptors was allowed to dwindle in favor of a more sustained analysis of the substructure of two prototypic receptors in which we had long-term vested interests—the GM-CSF receptor and the LIF receptor.

Answers were still required on how receptors such as these delivered a multiplicity of instructions to responding cells. Work in our sister Ludwig Institute by Andrew Wilks and his group had led to the discovery of a JAK kinase involved in phosphorylating and activating receptors that themselves possessed no kinase domain and thus no capacity to activate themselves by transphosphorylation. Additional JAK kinases were isolated by other groups and the JAKS were shown to activate a second set of signaling molecules, the STATS, which when phosphorylated could dimerize and translocate to the nucleus. These discoveries were exciting and offered a possible mechanism by which a receptor could transmit a signal that reached the nucleus. An immediate problem was then to determine whether different regions of the cytoplasmic domains of a receptor interacted with different JAKS and STATS in some combinatorial manner to generate qualitatively different signals.

An initial step was clearly to mutagenize receptor cDNAs to establish which regions could be associated with particular types of signals. Initial progress had been made by other workers using the simpler homodimeric receptors for erythropoietin and G-CSF. This work had defined a C-terminal region as being involved in differentiation and/or maturation signals and a second region closer to the membrane—the Box 1–Box 2 region—as being related to mitotic signaling. We set out, using the LIF receptor and the signaling β-chain of the GM-CSF receptor, to extend this work using transfected receptor cDNAs in the leukemic cell lines, WEHI-3B and M1. Neither system allowed information to be gathered on mitotic signaling, so additional systems using FDC-P1 and BaF/3 cell lines were included.

This work, which continues, has succeeded in providing quite detailed information on the role being played by various sections of the GM-CSF and LIF receptors. This is proving to be a complex subject because the various active regions do vary somewhat according to the type of cell in which they act, a situation requiring the use of multiple cell models for each question being posed.

In the course of our work on LIF and its receptor, it became evident that serum contained an agent that was able to bind to and block the action of LIF on responding cells. This LIF-binding protein was purified by us and, on sequencing, proved to be a soluble version of the extracellular domain of the LIF receptor. This was of considerable biological interest because serum concentrations of this soluble receptor were quite sufficient to block the action of any circulating LIF. As shall be discussed later, LIF had been presenting a major intellectual problem because of its bizarre range of multiple actions on different tissues. There was no situation in which the simultaneous occurrence of these multiple actions would make any sort of sense. Like most hematopoietic regulators, LIF is produced in multiple organs. The existence of high circulating levels of soluble LIF receptor would be able to confine the action of LIF to its site of production and avoid the occurrence of unwanted side actions.

Such circulating soluble receptors had already been documented for IL-2 and IL-6, although in the case of IL-6 the situation was quite different in that the soluble receptor-IL-6 complex was actually capable of delivering an IL-6 signal by interacting with any cell expressing the partner gp130 receptor chain. In general, however, high circulating levels of soluble receptors appear to be a stratagem adopted by the body to confine cellular responses to regions of local regulator production.

Our work with receptors and signaling continues to be a major part of our research programs because many fundamental questions about regulator action remain unresolved and are central to a proper understanding of how regulators exert their actions on responding cells.

FOURTEEN

The Role of the CSFs
in Myeloid Leukemia

Although in the period from 1968 to 1984 our laboratory had a sustained preoccupation with the characterization, purification, and mass production of CSFs, there were periods when, from our publications, this seemed not to be the case. In such periods many of the publications concerned the behavior of myeloid leukemic cells.

The possible involvement of regulators such as the CSFs in the initiation and emergence of myeloid leukemias was in fact the reason why we initially began working on the CSFs and such questions were of continuing importance to us. This is exemplified by our post-CSF work on leukemia inhibitory factor and the SOCS gene family encoding modulators of cytokine signaling in leukemic cells. We have always been a cancer research group, supported largely by cancer funds, with an understanding of leukemia as our major objective. It was inevitable that this would be reflected in the type of studies we undertook and the publications resulting.

From the outset of our work on the CSFs, we spent much effort to establish whether or not CSF levels were unusually high or low in leukemia—either human or murine. The initial hypothesis was that if the CSFs were proliferative factors for normal and also leukemic cells, then high CSF concentrations would enhance the proliferation of leukemic cells and the CSFs would be proleukemogenic agents tending to encourage the emergence or expansion of myeloid leukemic populations.

The overall data we gathered on serum or urine CSF levels suggested that these levels were neither consistently nor notably elevated in myeloid leukemia. On many of the occasions when serum or urine CSF levels were clearly elevated, there was a confounding intercurrent infection and the observed CSF levels may merely have been elevated in response to these infections.

These CSF data, when assessed retrospectively, would seem not to support the original simple proleukemic hypothesis. The major necessary caveat is, however, that serum CSF levels may provide an entirely misleading estimate of local CSF concentrations in tissues such as the bone marrow. To date, no technical method has been developed to estimate such local concentrations. A final answer to this apparently simple question about CSF concentrations in myeloid leukemia is, therefore, still not available and the original elementary hypothesis cannot be firmly excluded.

Following the development by Bill Robinson and Beverley Pike in 1970 of a workable method for culturing human granulocyte-macrophage progenitor cells in agar, we and others immediately sought to establish whether leukemic cells from humans with acute or chronic myeloid leukemia could proliferate clonally in agar cultures and, if so, whether such clonogenic leukemic cells were dependent on CSF for cell proliferation, as is the case for normal cells. Two possible alternatives were that the leukemic cells would proliferate in an autonomous manner, requiring no extrinsic stimulation, or that a mixed answer might be obtained in which a certain level of apparent autonomy would be exhibited but that additional proliferation could be achieved by using CSFs—either because additional clonogenic cells could be induced to proliferate or because individual clonogenic cells could then generate larger numbers of progeny.

With cells from patients with chronic myeloid leukemia (CML) the answers were relatively unambiguous and in good agreement between individual laboratories. By 1973 it was clear that CML cells could generate colonies of granulocytic and macrophage cells that were superficially normal in size and cellular maturation and this colony formation was absolutely dependent on CSF stimulation, using essentially the same concentrations as were required by normal cells.

There was in fact a certain initial confusion (as was also the case with the culture of normal human marrow cells) because many workers observed some colony formation in the absence of added CSF. Such "spontaneous" colony formation was quickly recognized to be cell concentration-dependent, suggesting that accessory cells in the cultures might endogenously produce the required CSF. Simple maneuvers such as prior removal of adherent accessory cells or their separation by density centrifugation essentially eliminated this spontaneous colony formation and when more sophisticated cell separation procedures succeeded in purifying the respective progenitor cells, all proliferation by CML and normal cells was unequivocally found to be CSF-dependent. The CSF-producing capacity of accessory cells (mainly monocytes and macrophages) was found to be essentially similar for CML and normal cells, indicating that the leukemic population did not exhibit an unusual capacity to produce CSF.

This body of information appeared at face value to indicate that, at the very least, CSFs (still not yet individually identified) would be mandatory cofactors in the development and progression of CML because the leukemic cells were dependent on CSF for proliferation. The ability of mature cells in the leukemic clone (monocytes) to produce their own growth factor was intriguing but, with even the relatively limited information available in 1973, was unlikely to mean too much because such monocytes were obviously not the only source of CSF in the body and possibly not a very important source. Furthermore, normal monocytes had an equivalent capacity to produce CSF yet normal granulocyte-macrophage populations certainly did not behave as leukemic cells.

The frequency of clonogenic cells in CML populations was high in the marrow and unusually high in the peripheral blood, as might be expected because the composition of cells in CML blood is not greatly different from that in the marrow.

The tidy uniformity of results from the culture of cells from patients with chronic phase CML did not last too long. Surprisingly, cells from CML patients in the acutely transformed and more aggressive stage of their disease did not grow well in agar cultures and commonly no colony formation was observed. The cells merely formed small clusters or did not proliferate at all. Why this should be so remains unexplained, but it was certainly an uncomfortable observation with cells that were now behaving in an aggressive manner in vivo.

Equally surprising was the fact that, although we documented that CML-derived colonies were derived from genuine members of the leukemic clone because the cells exhibited the Philadelphia chromosome abnormality, the colony cells when resuspended and recultured exhibited no further capacity for colony formation. The colony-forming cells appeared to have no capacity for self-generation, and the colony cells themselves seemed genuinely to have exhibited terminal differentiation. This terminal differentiation was not in itself worrying because the majority of CML cells in the patient do exhibit good maturation. However, the leukemic population in an untreated patient does expand progressively, so a major property of the clonal population—that of self-renewal by at least some members of the clone—was not being detected in the agar cultures.

Reflection on this problem suggested two possibilities to us and others. The first possibility was that the CSFs—although necessary for proliferation—might be having a second action, enforcing differentiation commitment and maturation in the responding cells. This possibility was to become well documented a decade later by work on appropriate leukemic cell lines using CSFs and particularly with the development of additional regulators such as LIF, IL-6, or oncostatin M (OSM). Indeed the purification of G-CSF had been monitored in part by using a maturation-inducing assay on WEHI-3B leukemic cells. When purified human CSFs became available, the same basic problem was observed in that each of the CSFs could stimulate colony formation by CML cells but in no instance were clonogenic cells present in the resulting colonies.

The second general possibility was that, although colony formation by CML cells was spectacular, in fact the culture technique was not able to detect the genuine ancestral, self-renewing, clonogenic cells in the leukemic population. It was merely detecting more mature clonogenic cells that were already on a one-way, CSF-dependent track of differentiation and extinction.

There remains to this day unease that the various clonal culture techniques so far used still have not succeeded in detecting the true clonogenic cells in CML and, if so, the dependency or otherwise of these more ancestral cells on extrinsic growth factors remains unresolved. A black hole therefore exists regarding the behavior and properties of the ancestral cells in CML clonal populations. What we know for certain is merely that the bulk of the progenitors are CSF-dependent and exhibit unremarkable properties. This may possibly be in sharp contrast to the properties of their antecedents. It may also be that in acute transformation, most of the cells are now of this ancestral type and are unable to be grown or analyzed by current methods. The apparent simplicity of CML populations has proved illusory for a complete understanding of the behavior of the key cells in the leukemic population.

If the behavior of CML cells looked promising and uncomplicated in early studies, the behavior of cells from patients with acute myeloid leukemia (AML) from the outset was puzzling and highly unsatisfactory. Despite the more aggressive nature of AML populations, they behaved in culture in very much the same manner as cells from acutely transformed CML patients. Cells from patients with apparently identical types of AML exhibited a widely varying capacity for clonal proliferation in vitro. More disturbingly, cells from most AML patients again were unable to form colonies but merely clusters of subcolony size. Some could form small colonies but these were always associated with an excess of clones of subcolony size. The cells in developing colonies and clusters usually exhibited a very poor capacity or no capacity for maturation. This indifferent performance in agar culture was surprising in view of the rapidly expanding nature of the populations as seen in vivo. The same reservations were raised about whether the genuine clonogenic cells in an AML population were being detected in these cultures. Buick and his colleagues in Toronto did develop an alternative culture system resulting in the development of a few small colonies of blast cells and these colonies did appear to contain clonogenic cells, suggestive of some capacity for self-generation by the initiating cells. These were held to be superior candidates for the true clonogenic cells in AML populations and this view continues to have some validity, although the observable capacity for self-generation is limited in magnitude and not wholly convincing.

As was the case for CML cells, we found that the cells from most patients with AML failed to exhibit spontaneous proliferation once accessory cells had been removed. Cells from some patients can exhibit what appears to be genuine autonomous growth in vitro but these are a small subset of AML patients. The proliferation of AML cells in vitro was able to be stimulated by CSFs in broadly similar concentrations to those active on normal cells, again leading to a conclusion that in AML, CSFs must also function as necessary cofactors in the emergence and progressive expansion of the leukemic clones.

This dominant pattern of dependency of human myeloid leukemic cells on CSF-containing material for proliferative activity was well established by 1975. When the four human CSFs were finally available in pure form the situation did not change substantially in that all four CSFs exhibited such activity, minor variations between individual leukemias possibly indicating no more than minor variations in levels of receptor expression on cells of different leukemias.

With this well established, the undoubted occurrence of some leukemias that could exhibit autonomous proliferation in vitro raised the speculation that at least some leukemias might be producing their own CSF as a conceivable mechanism for their autonomous proliferation. Attempts to obtain evidence for this in other laboratories did appear to uncover examples of production of biological activity resembling CSF and later evidence also included the detection of CSF mRNA in leukemia samples. Further work by these groups in the United States and the Netherlands extended these observations, but two problems were recognized that made it difficult to reach firm conclusions. The first was that CSF production was clearly inducible by handling of the cells in vitro, making it difficult to establish levels of activity actually existing in vivo. IL-1 was shown to be a major inducer of CSF production in such circumstances. Second and related, it was necessary to attempt to obtain answers on the clonogenic cells themselves because, in AML, maturing leukemic monocytes, like corresponding normal cells, do have some capacity to produce CSF. Few of the experiments performed were able to exclude these possible sources of misinterpretation and the actual situation in most leukemias remains unclear. Even when active CSF production was able to be demonstrated for some leukemic populations, this again would be occurring in the context of the whole body where there are numerous alternative tissue sources of CSF. On this basis, the phenomenon of autocrine production would be unlikely to have much significance unless there was something highly unusual happening when autocrine CSF production occurred in a responsive cell.

In our laboratories, we had put work on the question of autocrine CSF production on hold after 1975, being mainly preoccupied by our attempts to purify and then clone the CSFs. In 1985, our colleagues in the Ludwig Institute decided to pursue these matters further by studies based on the CSF-dependent cell line FDC-P1, which, although immortalized and incapable of maturation, is nonetheless not leukemogenic. Immediately preceding this new endeavor, Wendy Cook, with our collaboration, had shown that the Abelson virus could transform FDC-P1 cells to autonomously growing leukemic cells with no evidence that they had acquired an autocrine capacity to produce CSF, a finding subsequently confirmed by other groups. Clearly, these cells could be transformed in a manner not requiring autocrine CSF production. Nevertheless these cells, in their immortalized state, are midway between normality and the leukemic state and seemed a useful target cell in which to formally test the autocrine hypothesis of cancer development. The specific proposal able to be tested was that an acquired capacity to self-produce a relevant CSF (either GM-CSF or Multi-CSF) could result in leukemic transformation.

In an innovative series of experiments, Richard Lang and Tom Gonda from the Ludwig Institute inserted the cDNA for GM-CSF into FDC-P1 cells using a retroviral promoter. In joint studies, we found that such cells immediately transformed to fully autonomous leukemic cells and displayed, as expected, a capacity to produce GM-CSF. Because nothing else had been done to the cells other than to insert an active GM-CSF cDNA, we felt that these results provided the first direct proof of the general autocrine hypothesis of cancer development.

When Tom Gonda and Richard Lang extended these studies by inserting the cDNA for IL-3 (Multi-CSF), the other CSF to which FDC-P1 cells are responsive, a generally similar outcome was observed. Again, prompt leukemic transformation with Multi-CSF production was observed by us, but this time certain oddities emerged. Some leukemias were unequivocally autonomous, as had been the case for cells transformed by GM-CSF. However, a few demonstrated a curious behavior reminiscent of human leukemic cells. Although they were leukemic and Multi-CSF-producing, their growth in agar remained dependent on addition of extrinsic CSF. Furthermore, some also showed the phenomenon of cell crowding dependency for what little autonomous activity they displayed.

This strange outcome provided food for thought. It seemed possible to transform an immortalized cell solely by inducing autocrine CSF production but for this sometimes not to be detectable in conventional agar cultures, where the cells remained dependent on extrinsic stimulation. This suggested that there could indeed be something very peculiar about autocrine growth factor production, being adequate for the apparently more difficult feat of achieving transformation, yet not adequate to confer autonomous growth in vitro. If this was possible, much of the extensive data from the in vitro culture of human myeloid leukemic cells might be misleading in implying that the cells were not autocrine producers of CSF because of their dependency on extrinsic CSF for growth in vitro.

In extending our work on FDC-P1 cells, John Rasko in our group explored the action of the Moloney virus and its possible ability to transform FDC-P1 cells to autonomous leukemic cells. The Moloney virus contains no transforming gene so transformation needs to involve host genetic changes due to the particular insertion site of the Moloney virus. In all the leukemic lines he generated, Moloney virus insertion had involved a rearrangement of the GM-CSF or Multi-CSF genes, associated with an acquired ability of the cells to produce GM-CSF and/or Multi-CSF. In all cases this resulted in fully autonomous cells.

A somewhat similar outcome was observed in a different biological system but again involving FDC-P1 cells. We had noted that when FDC-P1 cells are injected into preirradiated mice, after a long latent period leukemias developed spontaneously that proved to be derived from the injected FDC-P1 cells. This outcome virtually never occurred in normal recipients and was the basis for the assessment that unmanipulated FDC-P1 cells are not leukemic. Analysis beginning in 1988 by Uli Dührsen of this delayed transformation of FDC-P1 cells in irradiated recipients documented in a sizable proportion of mice, that the leukemic cells were now producing GM-CSF and/or Multi-CSF based

Nick Nicola, Nick Gough, Larry Rohrschneider, Uli Dührsen, and Jean-Luc Villeval being visited by the Duke of Edinburgh.

on activation of the genes by insertion of an intracisternal A-particle upstream of the genes. The irradiation could not have directly induced translocation of intracisternal A-particles because the FDC-P1 cells involved had never actually been irradiated, merely the mice later receiving the cells. What irradiation had achieved, however, was the build-up of much larger numbers of FDC-P1 cells in the marrow, spleen, and lymph nodes than occurs in normal recipients. This presumably allowed many-fold more FDC-P1 cells to exist in the mice and to be at risk of transformation.

The peculiar importance of *autocrine* CSF production was again emphasized in 1993 when I carried out a somewhat similar study of the behavior of the FDC-P1 cells after injection into GM-CSF transgenic mice that have a constant vast excess of circulating GM-CSF, one of the growth factors to which FDC-P1 cells are highly responsive. Such animals developed over a period of a few months a very high frequency of leukemias that again were derived from the injected FDC-P1 cells, probably in part because of the very high numbers of FDC-P1 cells able to build up in the recipients with their high GM-CSF levels. What was

interesting, however, was that all these leukemias were autocrine producers of GM-CSF and/or Multi-CSF with evidence of rearrangement
of their genes. It is very difficult to imagine why the autocrine production of GM-CSF should have had the slightest relevance for the behavior of the FDC-P1 cells because they were already residing in a sea of
GM-CSF, nevertheless it *did* seem to matter.

I later carried out an experiment to challenge the by then established
dogma that regulators act on cells only by activating their high-affinity
membrane receptors. I set out to establish what would happen to cells
that produced and responded to GM-CSF if these cells lacked high-
affinity membrane receptors for GM-CSF. Would some type of cellular
response still be observable either because of interaction with low-
affinity receptors or because the CSF being produced within the cells
could have some direct action within these cells independent of any
necessary complexing with high-affinity receptors? The actual animal
generated by cross-breeding was a GM-CSF transgenic mouse lacking
the GM-CSF β-common chain receptor and thus having no high-
affinity receptors. To my disappointment, the results were spectacularly
negative. No abnormalities in target cells were observable in these
mice, unlike the situation usually developing in GM-CSF transgenic
mice. The outcome supported the dogma that growth factors act only
by activating their cognate membrane receptors. This casts some doubt
on one possibility for CSF-producing transformed leukemic cells—that
the CSF is peculiarly important because it acts in some odd manner
inside the cell. Of course transformed CSF-producing FDC-P1 cells do
also produce cognate receptors. They might still behave in an atypical
manner therefore if receptors meet their ligand intracellularly, but a
receptor-independent action of GM-CSF within the cell seems unlikely
because of the lack of any evidence for such an action.

What these various experiments with CSFs and transformation did
introduce was the recognition that autocrine growth factor production
can be leukemogenic in certain situations. Further, by allowing the
build-up of large populations of CSF-responsive, but possibly abnormal
cells, high CSF levels could indirectly allow a leukemia-transforming
event to occur more frequently and thus be indirectly leukemogenic.

What was odd in all of our work with the transformation of FDC-P1
cells was how often autocrine CSF production seemed to be the basis

for transformation and autonomous growth in vitro. This may have been an unfortunate skewing of the situation due to the peculiarities of FDC-P1 cells. In principle, there are many other ways in which a cell could acquire a capacity for autonomous proliferation and many of these have been demonstrated not only to result in autonomous proliferation but also, often as a much delayed consequence, in leukemic transformation. Thus, insertion of constitutively activated receptors in cells can confer an autonomous proliferative capacity on the cells, as can insertion of cDNAs encoding products likely to be, or to influence, mitotic signaling intermediates between the receptor and the nucleus in responding cells.

The actual cellular abnormalities leading to immortalization in a cell line like FDC-P1 have yet to be clarified but presumably these must somehow block the ability of the cells to choose to enter an irreversible pathway of commitment and terminal maturation. That this acquired abnormality in the commitment process, resulting in an abnormal capacity for self-renewal, is a key change involved in leukemogenesis was shown experimentally by Andrew Perkins and Suzanne Cory in the laboratories adjacent to ours. When they cotransfected cDNA for Hox-2.4, a gene able to influence commitment decisions, together with cDNA for Multi-CSF, normal marrow cells were immediately transformed to leukemic cells. Hox-2.4 is unlikely to be the only gene product with this relevant action but the model served as a prototype to identify the two types of abnormality necessary, or able, to induce the transformation of normal to leukemic cells. Again, in this model autocrine CSF production was involved but other methods for achieving autonomous proliferation would likely have been equally effective.

Our work on the proleukemogenic actions of the CSFs has been described as a continuum of experiments that overlapped the final phases of CSF purification and cloning, then extended into the post-cloning period. The actual situation in our laboratories was more complex still, because proceeding in parallel was yet another series of experiments on CSF action on leukemic cells that were addressing an opposite possibility—namely that CSF action might actually suppress the emergence of myeloid leukemic clones.

Logically, this latter stream of studies might have been expected to have been initiated by us in the early 1980s, as soon as it became evident that the CSFs were not merely growth factors but had actions in inducing commitment and maturation. These latter theoretically could represent suppressive actions when leukemic cells were involved. The crucial aspect of all cancer cells, including leukemic cells, is the ability of at least some ancestral cells in the neoplastic clone to exhibit an abnormally high capacity for self-renewal. This is necessary to ensure continuous expansion of the neoplastic clone—the more so if, as is the case with CML, many neoplastic cells become extinguished by terminal maturation and subsequent death.

In actual fact, as recounted earlier, our interest in the potential suppressive actions of CSF in myeloid leukemic cells had been aroused much earlier by experiments of Ichikawa in 1969 and 1970 and by our concurrent early culture work using human myeloid leukemic cells, where the necessary use of CSF as a mitotic stimulus was accompanied by a surprising failure of such colony cells to proliferate when recultured, possibly as a double consequence of CSF action.

For our work exploring the actions of GM-CSF and G-CSF on the leukemic cell line WEHI-3B, we had chosen not to use suspension cultures of leukemic cells but rather the original method used by Ichikawa of growing colonies in agar then looking for signs of maturation by reduced colony numbers and size or the development of coronae of differentiating cells around central colony areas. These parameters seemed to offer more sensitive detection methods because a small number of differentiating cells in a colony population could readily reveal themselves by their migratory behavior in agar.

GM-CSF had been found to have some capacity to suppress WEHI-3B colonies and induce maturation, but G-CSF had a much stronger action that we then used as one of our bioassays in purifying G-CSF. In our publications at that time we commented on the possible future clinical use of G-CSF in favorable cases of myeloid leukemia. In such patients, the use of G-CSF might suppress self-generation in the leukemic population and the G-CSF would not only be nontoxic for surviving normal marrow cells but would actually be a useful proliferative stimulus for them.

This possibility has yet to find a useful clinical application, mainly because most leukemias are refractory to differentiation induction by the CSFs while still retaining responsiveness to proliferative stimulation.

While this work had vindicated our belief that the CSFs can have suppressive actions on leukemic cells, yet at the same time be growth factors, we remained unsatisfied that the various studies, particularly those on M1 cells, could necessarily all be interpreted as due to the actions of one or other CSF.

In 1986 we decided to have a fresh look at the situation with a new Ph.D. student, Doug Hilton. We chose this time to use the M1 leukemic cell line and, as starting material, medium conditioned by Krebs II ascites tumor cells—a system used in the Ichikawa/Rehovot studies. Our plan was to completely fractionate this material, then to determine with a battery of assays exactly what CSFs were present and whether another agent might also be present in this material, as was being suggested by the more recent biochemical studies of Tomida and his colleagues in Sapporo.

This project proceeded very smoothly with our experienced team and by 1987 we had not only established that this ascites tumor-conditioned medium contained GM-CSF and G-CSF but also a novel glycoprotein that we had purified under the name leukemia inhibitory factor (LIF). This latter factor seemed possibly to be the differentiation (D) factor purified earlier by the Tomida-Hozumi group but, at the time, this was not certain and, perhaps a little unfairly, we chose to be cautious in our assumptions and named our molecule LIF. In 1987, we cloned a cDNA for murine LIF, then one for human LIF, and the name LIF had become established in the literature before sequence data finally revealed the D-factor to be the same molecule as LIF.

In general, I believe it to be bad manners to rename molecules, but the actual identity of the various candidate molecules inducing differentiation in M1 cells was still a very confused subject in 1987 and we felt that the fewer assumptions made about the identity or nonidentity of various candidate factors the better. This view has turned out to be wise. In a somewhat bizarre series of events, parallel studies on M1 cells in Rehovot resulted in the purification of a highly active differentiation-inducing factor that on sequencing turned out to be the known regulator IL-6. That two teams using the same cell line for their assays could arrive at two different purified molecules was decidedly odd. The explanation uncovered by Joseph Lotem in Rehovot was that distinct subline differences had developed between various M1 leukemic cell lines being maintained in Rehovot, Sapporo, and Melbourne. The Rehovot subline was unresponsive to LIF and responsive to IL-6, while our subline was much more responsive to LIF even though, at much higher concentrations, IL-6 has a more powerful action on our M1 cells than LIF. Clearly the original starting material had a complex mixture of active molecules—not only GM-CSF and G-CSF but also LIF and IL-6 and no doubt a number of other regulators. The need for caution about assuming the identity or nonidentity of these various active molecules was, in retrospect, warranted.

The time lapse between our decision to focus our resources on the purification and cloning of LIF (July 1986) and our filing of a patent application on LIF cDNA (September 1987) was barely more than a year and remains for us the gold standard for work of this type, even a decade later. We did not achieve success in the absence of competition. We knew that we were starting the LIF project *after* another group had published the purification of what was quite possibly the same molecule, and it had to be presumed that this group also had the goal of cloning a cDNA for this factor. What we did not know was that Genentech, one of the giants in U.S. biotechnology, had had LIF cloning as a major project for some time but was cleanly beaten by us, possibly because of our more focused approach, tighter teamwork, and superior experience.

Our decision not to publish a word on our biochemical and biological work on LIF until after filing of our patent application and publication of the cloning paper was not one needing to be enforced on us by AMRAD, our new industrial partner. We had learned this lesson from our G-CSF experience and were determined never to be pre-empted in this manner again. As a consequence, publication of the biochemical purification of LIF, the factor content of Krebs II ascites fluid, and the in vitro biological properties of LIF did not occur until 1988 and 1989.

The IL-6 and LIF discoveries were to mark an abrupt watershed in ideas about regulators. To this point, for those of us working on regulators active on hematopoietic populations, a neat enough compartmentalization had been possible. Factors active on lymphoid cells appeared to be quite distinct from those active on nonlymphoid hematopoietic cells. Thus IL-1 and IL-2 were active on T-cells but clearly had no actions on myeloid cells while conversely the CSFs and erythropoietin equally obviously seemed to have no actions on lymphoid cells. IL-4, with actions on lymphoid cells, did have some vague synergistic actions on myeloid cells but this was not sufficient to upset the neat-enough compartmentalization.

IL-6 proved to be a troublesome molecule in this context. It clearly had important actions on B-lymphoid cells yet later we found it able to stimulate granulocyte colony formation and it was clearly a powerful agent in inducing differentiation in myeloid leukemia cells. Notions of disturbing polyfunctionality regarding IL-6 and its actions on other tissues were beginning to be raised by Kishimoto and his colleagues in Osaka.

LIF proved to be a feral cat among the pigeons and notions about lineage specificity of regulators have never been the same since. In quick succession, LIF, a molecule purified for its differentiation-enforcing actions on myeloid leukemic cells turned out to be the despair of a number of other groups who had been busily engaged using other cell systems to try to characterize their favorite molecules. In a series of experiments triggered by some astute lateral thinking by Nick Gough and Lindsay Williams of the EMBO Laboratories, LIF was shown to be the sought-for active factor *suppressing* differentiation commitment in normal embryonic stem cells—a bizarre reversal of its action on leukemic cells. LIF also proved to be the factor switching autonomic neurones from adrenergic to cholinergic signaling, one of the factors inducing liver cells to produce acute-phase proteins and a cahexia-inducing molecule able to block lipid transport into adipocytes. Other unusual actions of LIF were stimulation of osteoblast proliferation, myoblast proliferation, megakaryocyte and platelet formation, production of ACTH by the pituitary, enhancement of the survival of sensory and motor neurones, and an ability to suppress spermatogenesis. Finally, LIF was shown to be absolutely essential for blastocyst implantation in the uterus.

Faced with the dilemma of understanding why the body would choose to use the same regulator for controlling such a bizarre miscellany of tissue types—a likely recipe for disaster because of unwanted side actions—certain facts emerged about what might prevent such unwanted actions. Like other regulators, LIF is produced locally in many tissues, for example, at the site of blastocyst implantation in the uterus. One possible explanation was that LIF, when needed, was essentially a local tissue product never intended to reach the circulation to act on other tissues. In the mouse at least, high levels of circulating soluble LIF receptor were shown by us to be present in the serum and to be able to effectively mop up any circulating LIF.

Conventional teaching on organ systems and their regulation has fostered the notion that the biology involved is distinct for each system. The disturbing polyfunctionality of LIF, IL-6, and other regulators is revealing that these older notions must somehow be incorrect. I believe that it is always wise to assume that the body does know what it is doing. The apparent illogicality of polyfunctional regulators must in fact not be so. It is our ideas on organ biology that are obviously in need of major revision. LIF has become a powerful agent for work on the suppression of leukemic cells but remains a problem child whose general behavior is yet to be resolved.

LIF presented us with some difficult decisions to be made. We had purified LIF as a candidate hematopoietic regulator able to suppress leukemic cells. LIF had also an ability to stimulate platelet production, another property warranting our continued interest in the molecule. While other groups were to document the full extent of its non-hematopoietic actions, we had already encountered many of these in our analysis of the pathology of mice with excess LIF levels using a model in which mice were engrafted with FDC-P1 cells overproducing LIF.

For a group skilled and experienced in hematopoiesis but faced with an agent with pleiotropic actions, there comes a time when studies on nonhematopoietic tissues should be abandoned and passed over to other groups with an interest and expertise in these areas. This we progressively did but there still remained a problem of whether, or how, LIF might be considered for possible clinical use.

Soon after its creation, our industrial partner AMRAD had entered into an agreement with Merck allowing AMRAD to market some of their more profitable pharmaceuticals in return for, among other things, Merck having access to the intellectual property of the Cancer Research Unit. Merck had an established interest in agents affecting bone metabolism and therefore exercised their right to take up the LIF option. An unsatisfactory two-year period followed during which Merck scientists failed to document reproducible actions of LIF on bone behavior using their range of assays. Merck therefore abandoned their rights to LIF and, in view of the ability of LIF to stimulate platelet formation, I suggested that Sandoz be approached for an expression of interest since they were already testing two platelet-stimulating agents—Multi-CSF and IL-6—for which they had patent positions. These studies were under way in their research institute in Vienna, which possessed a primate colony.

An agreement was entered into with Sandoz to produce pharmaceutical-grade human LIF and to carry out initial primate toxicity and biological studies on the stimulation of platelet production. After the slow production of LIF of the required homogeneity, these studies in primates were completed and published in 1992. The actions of LIF and IL-6 in stimulating platelet formation were comparable and possibly represented a potential clinical use. Nevertheless, Sandoz lost interest in further progressing studies with LIF and abandoned its rights in 1994. The rights were then assigned to Chugai with the intent of further developing the Sandoz-produced material, but this was not further progressed, probably due to the appearance in 1995 of a much stronger platelet-stimulating factor in the form of thrombopoietin.

LIF has now returned to be further developed by AMRAD, this time as an agent promoting neuronal survival and regeneration. Initial toxicity trials on systemically administered LIF commenced in Melbourne and the United Kingdom in 1998.

The polyfunctional regulators LIF and IL-6 made it possible to contemplate new studies on the nature of leukemic cell suppression and these were soon joined by two other polyfunctional regulators, oncostatin M (OSM) and IL-11, that also had comparable actions on M1 leukemic cells.

Although this quartet of regulators has the common feature of sharing the same gp130 receptor chain, our experiments and experiments in other laboratories using M1 cells transfected with cDNAs for other types of receptors indicated that there is nothing particularly novel about signals coming from the gp130 chains. For example, we found

Warren Alexander, Andrew Elefanty, Don Metcalf, Nick Nicola, Glenn Begley, and Doug Hilton.

that M1 cells expressing the transfected thrombopoietin receptor, Mpl, can then be effectively suppressed by the action of thrombopoietin and a similar outcome can be achieved using a variety of receptor-ligand pairs. Because the intracellular signaling regions of these receptors differ in amino acid sequence and, in some cases, in the initial signaling intermediates they activate, there would appear to be a number of ways in which a receptor can initiate a signaling cascade that will cause M1 leukemic cells to cease self-generation and initiate maturation. Logic suggests that a final common pathway should exist in the cell to mediate such responses, but it would seem that whether or not a particular regulator is active on M1 cells is simply a question of whether the appropriate receptors are expressed.

M1 leukemic cells are not typical of most myeloid leukemias in their ability to be induced to terminate self-renewal and to exhibit maturation. We have spent much effort to establish why other leukemias may be refractory, by exploring ways in which responsive M1 cells can be converted to similarly unresponsive leukemic populations. Use of a mutagen to precipitate such a conversion resulted in a number of refractory lines, some of which were found to have become refractory simply because of failure to produce and display the gp130 receptor chain.

In a more novel series of studies in our laboratories by Doug Hilton and Robyn Starr, a cDNA library from the immortalized line FDC-P1 was transfected into M1 cells in an attempt to obtain M1 colonies that resisted the differentiation-inducing action of IL-6. From one such colony, the inserted cDNA was found to encode a novel protein, SOCS-1. Production of this protein is highly inducible by IL-6 and a number of other cytokines and blocks phosphorylation and activation of JAK-1, gp130, and then STAT-3 as the likely mechanism of the suppressing action for IL-6-initiated signaling. This suppressive action is not restricted to signals from the IL-6 receptor but also restricts, by differing mechanisms, signaling in various cells from the interferon-γ receptor and the receptors for GM-CSF and SCF. When Warren Alexander generated mice that lacked the SOCS-1 gene, a neonatally lethal syndrome developed that involved massive liver damage and infiltration of the skin, pancreas, heart, and lung with granulocyte and macrophage populations. Cells from SOCS-1 –/– mice displayed an intrinsic hypersusceptibility to the action of interferon-γ and administration of antibodies to interferon-γ or crossing the mice with interferon-γ –/– mice to produce a double knockout mouse completely prevented disease development.

SOCS-1 could well be a candidate molecule that is active in some leukemias or dysplastic populations preventing their proper maturation or cessation of self-generation in response to regulator signaling. However, examination of the expressed sequence tags databases revealed that a family of 20 proteins shares a sequence relationship with the SOCS box C-terminal region of SOCS-1, seven of these having a similar general structure to SOCS-1. In particular, SOCS-3 appears closely related to SOCS-1 and is equally effective in suppressing M1 responses to IL-6 and related cytokines. Many members of this SOCS family may have quite unrelated actions and may merely share a SOCS region that can interact with elongins A and B to target such molecules for endosomal degradation. Nevertheless, some members of this group could also be candidates for modulators of cytokine signaling and be of possible relevance in explaining why myeloid leukemias so often do not become suppressed by cytokine action.

The possibility remains, however, that CSF and other cytokines *do* in fact suppress leukemic cell self-renewal in a parallel action as they stimulate leukemic cell proliferation. This may be the reason why leukemic clonogenic cells exhibit little evidence of self-renewal in agar cultures.

The possible role of the CSFs and other cytokines in the emergence, expansion, or suppression of myeloid leukemias is a story that has gone through many twists and turns in the 30 years since the questions began to be posed. In truth, we may barely have scratched the surface of this complex area and are far from establishing a satisfactory picture that encompasses and explains the large body of confusing observations that have accumulated. There *is* a role being played and it is likely to be important, but exactly how and why remain questions for future work to resolve.

In the face of these continuing uncertainties, clinicians have justifiably been hesitant to use CSFs in the management of myeloid leukemias. CSFs have been deliberately used prior to chemotherapy to stimulate leukemic cell proliferation and hence render the cells more susceptible to cycle-specific chemotherapeutic agents. This appears to be achievable without detriment to the likelihood of achieving an initial remission but what long-term advantages there may be from such a strategy have yet to be established. No one has yet had the courage to use CSFs during remission in an attempt to suppress any surviving leukemic cells. This procedure might work in principle but only if the cells involved were responsive to suppression by CSFs. More needs to be established about the in vitro responsiveness of such cells before such a maneuver would be ethically justifiable, given the growth stimulating action of the CSFs on leukemic cells.

FIFTEEN

In Vivo Manipulation of CSF Genes

After two decades of increasingly sophisticated reductionist in vitro analyses of hematopoietic biology, it might seem highly curious that many of us in the mid-1980s were planning seriously for a return to whole-animal experiments. This was more unexpected and seemingly unnecessary because results were beginning to show that injected CSFs were active in vivo and producing responses in accord with expectations from prior in vitro studies.

The initial in vivo experiments were designed to determine the consequences of extremely high or prolonged elevations of growth factor levels in vivo, one of the consequences uppermost being the possible development of leukemia under these conditions. These considerations were to lead to an initial series of transplant studies using mice engrafted with hematopoietic cells genetically engineered to overproduce growth factors. These studies overlapped parallel experiments carried out by our Ludwig Institute colleagues in which transgenic GM-CSF mice were developed with a similar set of objectives.

In the background were a more elaborate and costly series of experiments to determine the consequences of inactivation of CSF genes on hematopoiesis in mice. These gene inactivation experiments were, in a sense, forced on us by a growing need to establish the precise role being played in vivo by each individual CSF. However, in no small measure, the experiments became necessary to counter growing criticism that the CSFs might not be the genuine regulators of basal blood cell production. The criticism being raised was that the CSFs had nothing to do with controlling basal hematopoiesis; they were only readily detectable in abnormal situations like infections and were merely accessory or emergency molecules used in times of acute need. If this was the case, nothing had been learned about normal basal hematopoiesis and a fresh search for the "real" regulators would need to be undertaken. This line of argumentation was to prove to have no substance but, to counter it, genetically manipulated animals of all types were generated by us and others. Working procedures had then to be developed for making a complete analysis of hematopoiesis in vivo—something that had been rather neglected during the previous two decades of increasingly sophisticated in vitro biology.

Today, most experimental hematopoiesis again is based on whole-animal studies and this switch during the past decade has highlighted a near-disastrous shortage of experimental biologists with sufficient experience to work with whole animals let alone make accurate diagnoses of disease pathology in such animals. This abrupt switch in experimental biology is now reaping the consequences of the previous overfascination of young graduates with molecular biology and its presumed ability to render cellular and whole-animal studies obsolete. Molecular biology is a powerful technology but is essentially useless without parallel expertise in cell biology and whole-animal analyses.

In the initial in vivo studies made by us after CSF cloning, the possible toxic effects of overproduction of CSFs were a central issue. Hematopoietic populations are very convenient for use in exploring such issues. Reasonably efficient viral vector systems were available for transfecting cDNA into hematopoietic cells and transfected marrow cells could then be used to repopulate irradiated recipients. Ideally, a mouse is generated by this maneuver in which some or most of the repopulating hematopoietic cells now constitutively overproduce the product of the transfected cDNA, resulting in a mouse with constantly elevated levels of the cDNA product—in our case, CSFs.

Greg Johnson in our group pursued these studies relentlessly and succeeded in generating, in sequence, repopulated mice with excess levels of GM-CSF, IL-3, and G-CSF. Serum levels of CSF were elevated to astonishingly high values with a spectacular consequent over-stimulation of the proliferation of responsive cells. In the case of GM-CSF, not only were blood, spleen, and marrow levels of granulocytes, monocytes, and eosinophils elevated but there was massive infiltration of the liver and lung by proliferating granulocyte-macrophage populations resulting in early death of the animals. The immediate question needing to be resolved was whether these populations were actually transformed leukemic cells. This appeared not to be the case because the cells failed to exhibit progressive proliferation on transplantation to normal recipients. The major disadvantage of this transplantation maneuver was that comparable progeny mice could not be bred from the transplanted mice. All experimental animals had to be individually generated by the cumbersome process of viral transfection of marrow cells followed by irradiation of recipient mice then transplantation of the transfected marrow cells.

The production of the first genetically transmissible (transgenic) model of GM-CSF overproduction was achieved synchronously with the Johnson studies with the generation in 1987 of transgenic GM-CSF mice by Richard Lang and colleagues in the Ludwig Institute. The additional GM-CSF genes in these mice were under the independent control of a strong viral promoter element. These mice also had elevated serum concentrations of GM-CSF, although not nearly as high as in the Johnson-type transplanted mouse model.

Somewhat disconcertingly, these GM-CSF transgenic mice did not show any changes in the number of granulocytes, macrophages, or eosinophils in the blood, marrow, or spleen as might have been expected from the Johnson experiments. However, the expression pattern achieved for the transgene was restricted mainly to macrophage populations in the peritoneal and pleural cavities and here the local excess levels of GM-CSF resulted in spectacular 100-fold elevations in macrophage numbers with the activation of certain but not all functions of these cells. Again this overproduction of GM-CSF and responding macrophages did not result in leukemic transformation.

The findings from the two mouse models of excessive GM-CSF levels began to establish a proposition that simple proliferative overstimulation is not by itself leukemogenic. On this question, models developed later by other workers and involving chronic overstimulation of the proliferation of various hematopoietic cells did seem, late in life, to lead in some instances to leukemic transformation. However, from the low frequency and sporadic nature of this transformation it is probable that additional genetic events were required, as was discussed earlier.

GM-CSF transgenic mice died prematurely in middle age with inflammatory lesions in various tissues, particularly muscle, and with evidence suggesting a general action of toxic products on the tissues. The interpretation of this tissue damage was that it was the consequence of GM-CSF overstimulating the massive additional numbers of macrophages to produce toxic agents like TNF, interferon-γ, etc—actions that had previously been documented for GM-CSF by in vitro studies. The findings coincided with data from patients being given unduly large doses of GM-CSF who exhibited the sporadic occurrence of what could have been similar inflammatory responses.

Greg Johnson followed his initial studies on GM-CSF with the development with Juliana Chang of additional transplantation models in which the regenerating hematopoietic cells were overproducing either G-CSF or Multi-CSF. Again, the achieved circulating levels of either factor were exceedingly high with consequent massive overproduction of the blood cell types known to respond to these agents in vitro and in vivo. The engrafted G-CSF-producing populations stimulated astonishingly high numbers of granulocytes to develop in the blood, marrow, and most tissues but the animals exhibited no obvious toxic effects of this overproduction and, in particular, there was no anemia or thrombocytopenia. Mice may not be an ideal model for documenting the consequences of neutrophil overload in the lungs but the findings did much to dismiss the possibility that a profound overproduction of one subpopulation of hematopoietic cells could deplete the stem cell capacity to generate other types of progeny—a theoretical possibility that had received much prior speculation.

Engrafted mice overproducing Multi-CSF displayed hyperplasia of a wide range of hematopoietic cells, as expected. However, the most striking response was the development of massive numbers of mast cells in multiple organs including the skin. The mice exhibited evidence of an itchy skin and developed chronic skin ulceration from scratching, an outcome that is likely to have contributed to their early death. In this, the murine model again predicted that similar problems might arise in humans injected with IL-3, as has proved to be the case with the occurrence in some patients of hypersensitivity responses.

Somewhat later a comparable model was developed by Jean-Luc Villeval in our laboratory involving the chronic overproduction of erythropoietin, which led to a sustained selective overproduction of red cells.

To a degree, these overproduction models provided valuable information on tissue pathology that might result from sustained excess levels of CSF and other regulators. The observed consequences were, however, explicable by known in vitro actions of the molecules and did not extend knowledge much more than that being obtained from the use of high dosages of CSFs in patients.

From these and concurrent studies on transgenic mice in other laboratories, it was becoming recognized that transgenic mice could exhibit some odd syndromes that seemed unlikely to be providing reliable information on the true in vivo biology of the agents. An obvious problem was in achieving gene transcription in various tissues that faithfully reproduced the pattern of transcription in normal tissues. The various promoters being used were resulting in overproduction in atypical locations and the resulting changes observed may have been the consequence of the atypical production sites of these regulators. Some skepticism arose regarding the relevance of some of the changes being observed and transgenic mice have fallen out of favor as preferred models for investigating the in vivo biology of the CSFs and comparable hematopoietic regulators. This situation could be retrieved if more physiologically relevant control elements for the transgenes could be developed.

In the meantime, there was a growing body of opinion that the most relevant information on the in vivo role of individual CSFs was going to require the development of mice with inactivation of the genes encoding the CSFs or their receptors. Furthermore, such animals could address the criticism that the CSFs actually played no role in the regulation of hematopoiesis under basal conditions.

Technology of generating mice with specific gene inactivations—knockout mice—was relatively new in the early 1990s. Nevertheless, Ashley Dunn, with Ed Stanley and Graham Lieschke in the Ludwig Institute, accepted the technical challenge and commenced efforts to generate GM-CSF and G-CSF knockout mice. Despite the claims of experts in this technology, the generation of a knockout mouse is still a tour de force that often takes one to two years, particularly if complications arise. The projects are both labor intensive and expensive in terms of required resources and become major enterprises that prevent other studies from being undertaken. Much, therefore, is gambled on the success of the enterprise—first, that some sort of viable mouse will result and, second, that interpretable changes will be observed. Characteristically, knockout mice take a long time to develop and, humans being somewhat impulsive, initial publications describing such mice are hasty affairs that always underestimate the abnormalities that are to be found in such animals. Indeed, it is likely that all knockout models require a decade of intensive study before even the most obvious abnormalities are recognized and adequately analyzed. For this reason, although CSF knockout mice were early in the field, many things remain unstudied about these mice.

Workers on M-CSF seem to have a charmed life. Not only did they not have to go through the pain of isolating a cDNA for the M-CSF receptor but, as matters turned out, they did not have to go to the bother of generating M-CSF knockout mice. In the mid-1970s, a naturally occurring mutant mouse (op/op) was described in which cortical bone tissue overgrew, resulting in occlusion of much of the marrow cavity and the disease state osteopetrosis. Experiments by Wiktor-Jedrzejczak and colleagues showed that, although macrophage numbers were low in these mice, levels of progenitor cells were actually elevated. This suggested that the mice could be lacking a macrophage-active CSF. The gene involved was localized to chromosome 3, and when later it was recognized that the location of the M-CSF gene was also somewhere in the same region on chromosome 3, it occurred to two groups to explore the possibility that the op/op mouse was in fact exhibiting the consequences of inactivation of the M-CSF gene. The particular rationale behind this lateral thinking was that new bone formation in mice is continuous and requires constant remodeling of the bones by osteoclasts. Osteoclasts were becoming recognized as specialized derivatives of macrophage precursors and there was some evidence implicating M-CSF as being able to stimulate osteoclast formation in vitro. Analysis of the M-CSF gene in op/op mice in 1990 revealed that it was indeed abnormal because insertion of an additional thymidine residue had put the remainder of the sequence out of frame, leading to an inability to transcribe and produce M-CSF.

The op/op mouse was therefore a ready-made M-CSF knockout mouse and analysis quickly confirmed that macrophage populations in these mice were severely depleted in many, but not all, tissues. Other more curious aspects of these mice were a failure of teeth to erupt and an inability of op/op mice to sustain pregnancy. These abnormalities were correctable by the injection of M-CSF. The observed major depletion in macrophage numbers was convincing evidence that M-CSF must play an important role under basal conditions in regulating macrophage production and particularly the formation of osteoclasts, despite its apparently indifferent performance when injected into animals or patients. This conclusion has remained valid and so M-CSF became the first of the CSFs to meet the criticism that CSFs might play no role in the basal physiology of hematopoiesis.

Equally clearly, macrophage numbers were not zero in such mice, so a second conclusion became possible, namely that other regulators must also play a role in regulating macrophage production. This theme was to recur in subsequent knockout work. None of the known regulators is solely responsible for controlling the production of any type of hematopoietic cell. The situation is not one of redundancy but of collaborative action by multiple regulators—the principle of collaborative action or synergy having been noted first in in vitro studies.

The first deliberate knockout of a CSF gene was achieved simultaneously in 1994 by Ed Stanley and Ashley Dunn in our sister Ludwig Institute and by Glen Dranoff and colleagues in Boston, the gene concerned being that encoding for GM-CSF. By this time, GM-CSF was well accepted as being able, on injection, to elevate white cell numbers and to have proliferative effects on various hematopoietic populations. If not apparently as strong as G-CSF, it nonetheless was active. The clear expectation was therefore that the GM-CSF −/− mouse would show some numerical defects in granulocyte, macrophage, and eosinophil populations. The GM-CSF −/− mice were born in the expected Mendelian ratio and appeared to be healthy. We carried out the initial analyses on hematopoietic populations in adult GM-CSF −/− mice and were astonished to observe no numerical defects in white cell levels in the blood or in the various populations in the marrow, spleen, and peritoneal cavity. A careful analysis by us of cultured marrow, spleen and peritoneal cells failed to detect anything unusual about the various progenitor cell populations or their responsiveness to stimulation. Our Boston colleagues made the same negative observations and reached the somewhat premature conclusion that GM-CSF was not a hematopoietic regulator under basal conditions.

However the situation changed radically when the –/– organs were examined histologically because both groups observed that all –/– mice had abnormal lungs with infiltrating granulocytic and macrophage populations, accumulations of surfactant and protein in the alveoli, and often small foci of infection. This is the disease state, alveolar proteinosis, and lack of stimulation by GM-CSF appears to lead to alveolar macrophage dysfunction as the basis for the disease. These GM-CSF –/– mice also died prematurely with a miscellany of indolent infections, again likely to be the consequence of macrophage hypofunction.

The outcome of these observations was that GM-CSF clearly was not a redundant regulator. While it appeared not to be necessary for the production of basal numbers of granulocytes, macrophages, and eosinophils, it played a necessary and unique role in regulating the functional activity at least of macrophages and possibly of other cell types.

Lorraine Robb and Catherine Drinkwater went on in our own laboratories to develop a mouse lacking the gene for the β-common chain of the GM-CSF receptor. These mice as a consequence have no high-affinity receptors for GM-CSF or IL-5, which require this signaling chain. These mice showed precisely the same changes as GM-CSF –/– mice, as expected, but in addition a profound depletion of eosinophils, showing that IL-5 is a major regulator of eosinophil production.

While these latter studies were in progress, Graham Lieschke and colleagues in the Ludwig Institute had developed a G-CSF –/– mouse. When we analyzed hematopoiesis in these mice in joint studies, a more conventional answer was obtained. The mice had abnormally low neutrophil levels in the blood and low levels of granulocytic cells in the marrow. Oddly enough, they also showed deficient numbers of all types of progenitor cells in the bone marrow. This seemed at first to be a strange situation but concurrent in vitro studies in our laboratories were beginning to show that, when G-CSF acts in collaboration with stem cell factor, the production of progenitor cells is enhanced in all lineages. Furthermore, when G-CSF is injected into mice or patients again the rise in progenitor cell numbers involved all lineages, not merely the granulocyte-committed lineage.

We were fairly comfortable therefore with the changes being observed in G-CSF –/– mice. G-CSF was clearly a major regulator of basal neutrophil production and was also necessary for proper granulocytic responses to challenge infections. Again, as was the case with M-CSF, loss of G-CSF did not reduce neutrophil levels to zero, so other agents must also play a role in regulating granulocyte production. G-CSF –/– mice were also found to die prematurely with indolent infections and cross-breeding to generate GM-CSF –/– G-CSF –/– mice yielded an animal that was even more susceptible to chronic infections, with often the development of amyloid disease before death.

To complete this set of experiments, Lorraine Robb and Catherine Drinkwater also generated mice lacking the gene encoding the private β-receptor chain for IL-3—the chain preferentially used in vivo for signaling by IL-3. These IL-3 β –/– mice showed very few changes except a hyporesponsiveness to stimulation in vitro by IL-3. Subsequently, we developed what amounts to a complete IL-3 –/– mouse by inactivating the genes for both the β-common chain and the private β-chain for IL-3. These mice revealed no obvious hematological abnormalities beyond those shown by βc –/– mice, raising the possibility that IL-3 might be a redundant regulator. Initial conclusions, however, usually underestimate the presence of abnormalities and mice of this type have subsequently been reported to exhibit subnormal responses to parasitic infection.

Our later experiments inactivating other hematopoietic receptor genes have produced a somewhat similar mixed bag of results. Knockout by Warren Alexander of the gene encoding the receptor for thrombopoietin produced a similar mouse to the thrombopoietin –/– mouse, both mice having profoundly reduced, but not zero, platelet levels and also deficiencies in stem cells and a broad range of hematopoietic progenitor cells of multiple lineages. This outcome clearly resembled that of inactivation of the G-CSF gene.

Conversely, while knockout of the IL-11 receptor gene produced no obvious hematological disease, the mice exhibited an inability to sustain pregnancy because of the development of highly abnormal placentas.

To date, the knockout approaches have validated the important role of M-CSF, GM-CSF, and G-CSF in basal hematopoiesis with some evidence for Multi-CSF having an important role at least in certain abnormal situations. Knockouts of other hematopoietic regulators or their receptors have produced similar evidence that each regulator does have a unique irreplaceable role in hematopoiesis and firmly rejects two hypotheses: (a) that there is regulator redundancy, and (b) that two types of regulator systems exist—one for basal conditions and one for emergency situations. The other general conclusions are that actions may not simply be apparent from cell numbers but may also involve cell function and that some actions may require time to become apparent or require assiduous experiments to reveal them.

More sophisticated versions of knockout mice are beginning to be widely used. These include insertion of the LacZ or GFP genes into the inactivated gene region, retaining the control elements of the deleted gene. Such mice provide valuable information on which cell types are transcribing the gene of interest in the body. Conditional knockout mice are in use where the gene need not be deleted in early stages of development but can be inactivated later in adult life. The most sophisticated current knockouts involve replacement of genes by genes with specific mutations, to model various leukemic or dysplastic states, where mutations have been noted in the genes encoding hematopoietic receptors.

SIXTEEN

The Bottom Lines

Not a day passes now when CSFs are not in use in experimental hematology laboratories for one type of experiment or another. In our case, we now most often seem to be using the CSFs to investigate the behavior of granulocyte-macrophage populations from mice with some form or other of gene manipulation. Certainly, not a day passes when patients somewhere are not receiving injections of CSF or transplants of CSF-elicited peripheral blood stem cells.

The CSFs have become part of the fabric of experimental hematology and clinical medicine. For our group, which uncovered the CSFs and stuck with them during their subsequent difficult gestation and development, this has been a satisfying outcome. With the passage of time, members of our team have come and gone. Of the 522 refereed papers and six books on the CSFs and related matters so far coming from studies in which we participated, there are in fact 329 scientists and clinicians as authors (see Appendix).

The cost of this work is difficult to calculate, but, in the case of GM-CSF, our largest single project in the area, we have estimated that it cost us in the Hall Institute in the region of U.S. $30,000,000. It has become the fashion of many governments these days to hope for financial returns from appropriate medical research. For the Hall Institute and Ludwig Institute our combined royalties from GM-CSF approxi-

The Cancer Research Unit, 1996.

mate $2,000,000 per year and, for a patent with a 10- to 15-year life, we will not recoup the money we spent on the GM-CSF project. For our G-CSF work we receive only nominal royalties from Australian sales of G-CSF by one company

This is an abysmal way of assessing medical research. Medical research includes, but is not merely, the intellectual exercise of discovering how the body and its various tissues develop and function. The primary objectives of medical research have always been to discover the nature of human diseases and, with this knowledge, to develop methods for disease prevention or cure. Medical research has therefore always been goal-oriented—the mastery of disease through discovery. Those undertaking medical research have become familiar with having to justify their research in a defensive manner—justifying to donors or government agencies why effort and money has been, or will be, expended properly in medical research. Justification, rather than exploitation, therefore becomes incorporated early into the ethos of all young research workers.

It can in fact be readily enough documented that the expense of undertaking medical research is cost-effective for the country, whether assessed on the economic value of lives saved, diseases prevented or shortened, or reduction in the cost of pre-existing treatment methods. Despite this, it is nonetheless true that major discoveries also result in major redistributions of health care money in the form of salaries for the doctors, nurses, and technicians who bring the new discovery into clinical use and new money to be earned by pharmaceutical and equipment companies. In the latter case, the money involved is potentially new wealth for the country concerned if the drug or procedure can be marketed widely.

Because of these latter considerations, it is possible to approach medical research with a simpler, self-serving, objective—to make money for a company or the country. In this approach, drug discovery leads directly to exploitation with little effort expended on understanding. The justification for this approach is simply that if the drug is useful, the population benefits, which is the stated goal anyway of medical research.

At issue therefore in the contrast between academic medical research and industrial research is whether the proper sequence is discovery–understanding–application or discovery–application (exploitation).

These are weighty matters of research policy. For our group during this period, our objectives were fairly simple—to try to relieve human suffering by advancing knowledge, not to build profitable business enterprises. Our own rewards have come from the completion of research projects of importance, performed with skill and sustained effort, that have added to our common store of knowledge and, of course, from the patients we occasionally encounter by accident who have benefited from our efforts.

We recognize very clearly that most medical research, however innovative and meticulously performed, does not have the reward of witnessing a consequent advance in medical practice, so we consider ourselves fortunate indeed to have been involved in one of these uncommon examples.

Being composed for the most part of Australians, who are competitive by nature, our group has also had the undoubted pleasure of pitting our skills against those of our international colleagues in fair competition. Despite what most believe, collegiality between scientists is largely a myth and tough competition the rule in medical research. Collegiality does exist but it is seen between the members of a group and is one of the continuing rewards of medical research when performed as a group.

After 35 years are we in any way satisfied that we have now completed our work on the CSFs? The answer is most certainly that we are not. We have made a good enough beginning but it is only a beginning.

From the restricted viewpoint of work on the CSFs, the knockout mice drew an important line under all the studies that preceded them. These studies completed the various phases that began with the discovery of biological activity in crude material, then saw the characterization and purification of the CSFs, the cloning of the CSF and receptor genes, the production of recombinant CSFs, and their use in patients with, finally, the gene manipulation studies documenting the unique role played in vivo by these regulators. It would be quite naïve however to assume that all information of importance regarding the CSFs has now been accumulated.

A critical appraisal of the story reveals many important defects in our understanding of the CSFs. We really have no reliable information on which cell types in what organs actually produce the various CSFs. What levels are produced and what are the concentrations achieved in various tissues? What triggers or regulates CSF production under basal or emergency conditions? What is the actual fate of the various CSF molecules produced? Is CSF production extremely efficient, with most of the molecules produced being consumed by acting on responding cells, or is the whole process enormously wasteful with most molecules being degraded or cleared by irrelevant cells? What are the organs that degrade or clear CSF and how do they recognize CSFs and degrade them? What is the extent and importance in actual life of CSF interactions, either with other CSFs or other regulators, in the stimulation of hematopoietic populations? While we have some knowledge regarding these latter questions in vitro, they relate mainly to actions on stem and progenitor cells and even these are quite incomplete. Virtually no information exists on CSF interactions on mature end cells.

A firm theoretical prediction is that regulators with stimulating actions cannot alone achieve stable cell production without the co-action of balancing inhibitory regulators. Some inhibitors have been described but these do not appear to be very satisfactory candidates and most lack sufficient lineage specificity. If inhibitors are indeed a key component of the control system operating on hematopoietic cells, inhibitor biology is very much an undeveloped science.

There are similar deficiencies in the current clinical uses of the CSFs. No serious effort has been made to duplicate the likely in vivo situation in which multiple regulators cooperate to achieve desired results. Most clinical work so far has used single-agent therapy. There is also a lack of logic in the timing of the use of these factors. To use stimulating factors *after* destruction of most target cells by chemotherapy is hardly the way to obtain optimal cellular responses. The whole area of the clinical use of CSFs in infections has not really been investigated thoroughly. Again, the prophylactic use of CSFs is often possible in the context of infections but has never been explored. There are various likely additional uses of the CSFs, particularly for GM-CSF, to accelerate chronic ulcer or wound healing or enhance vaccines, but these remain anecdotal and urgently need proper testing.

Our information on the possible role of CSFs in the development of specific diseases is minimal. Osteopetrosis in humans, unlike in the mouse, may not involve abnormal M-CSF function. Alveolar proteinosis in humans at least can be based on aberrant GM-CSF production or defective GM-CSF receptors. While excess levels of GM-CSF can lead to chronic inflammatory states experimentally, what diseases in humans are of a comparable general nature and based on GM-CSF? How often is poor resistance to infections based on defective production or action of CSFs and, if so, what are the particular infections involved? The role being played by the CSFs in human myeloid leukemia remains unresolved.

Answers to many of these unresolved problems can be obtained, given sufficient effort, but regrettably few workers seem to have the motivation to dig more deeply into a subject that, while clearly of importance, no longer has the novelty prized by granting agencies or scientific journals.

In my more gloomy moments it is evident to me that we have barely scratched the surface of regulator biology, including the CSFs.

Seen in retrospect, the 35-year saga of the CSFs had early goals that at times seemed unattainable—the purification and cloning of the CSF—but were in fact eventually achieved with persistence. At that time the story seemed to have reached a natural conclusion but of course the reality was different. We became entangled in an equally complex struggle to characterize CSF receptors then their signaling systems—the latter being a very open-ended goal where again no complete answers seem attainable in the foreseeable future. We have witnessed and have ourselves become deeply involved in a return to the complexity of whole-animal studies, granted with exquisitely selective tools in gene inactivation, but with uncharacterizable modulations of anything observed.

The days of factor purification now seem remote indeed and to have represented an important, but only a single small step, along the way. The exquisitely selective lock and key system of the regulator and its receptor is the one small island of specificity and certainty between the unknown complexities of the whole body in health or disease and the equally confusing complexity of the intracellular signaling networks.

This island of certainty has to be the base for further expeditions into both areas of the unknown and we are pleased to have helped build this small island. Perhaps, with persistence, we will identify and develop other islands in this archipelago of life. We can but continue to try, trusting as always in the support and friendship of able colleagues, equally willing to undertake adventures into the unknown.

Appendix

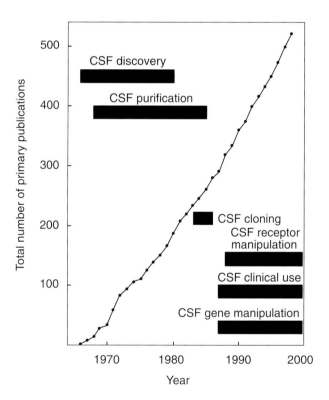

The cumulative number of primary publications dealing with colony stimulating factors and related matters of which Cancer research unit members were authors or coauthors with the periods of various major projects indicated.

Authors and coauthors of refereed publications in the period from 1966 to 1998 involving one or more members of the cancer research unit on the colony-stimulating factors and related matters referred to in this account.

Numbers following names are the number of publications.

Ada G	1	Campbell L	1
Alexander WS	16	Carroll GJ	1
Allan EH	1	Cary D	5
Allen JD	1	Cebon J	14
Alton NK	1	Chan SH	11
Aplan PD	1	Chang JM	5
Barnett L	1	Cheers C	4
Bartlett PF	3	Chester HM	2
Basser RL	7	Cherington V	1
Basu S	1	Chopra R	1
Bath ML	1	Chumbley G	1
Battye FL	7	Claesson MH	6
Begley CG	67	Clark C	1
Billington T	1	Clark MR	3
Bilski-Pasquier G	2	Clark RL	1
Body J	1	Clark SC	2
Bollum FJ	1	Cline MJ	3
Bonnem E	1	Cobbold SP	3
Bowtell D	1	Coghlan JP	1
Boyd AW	9	Cook WD	2
Boyd J	2	Cooper PC	3
Bradley TR	14	Corcoran LM	1
Brown MA	7	Cory S	3
Brown TC	1	Cross BA	2
Buckley J	1	Curtis D	3
Buirski G	1	Cutler RL	4
Burgess AW	50	Cuthbertson RA	2
Burns GF	2	Dao C	2
Camakaris J	1	David JR	2
Cambier N	1	Dauer R	1

Decker T	1	Gough J	2
DeLamarter J	3	Gough NM	46
Delmonte L	3	Grail D	6
De Luca E	8	Green AR	9
Dessein A	3	Green M	9
Dexter TM	1	Greenberger JS	1
Di Rago L	4	Grigg AP	7
Dranoff G	1	Grigoriadis G	2
Dresch C	2	Grumont RJ	3
Drinkwater CM	2	Gunz FW	1
Dunn AR	14	Gutman GA	1
Dührsen U	12	Haigh AM	1
Edwards SJ	1	Hall B	1
Elefanty AG	4	Hamilton JA	4
Elliott MJ	4	Handman E	4
Elwood NK	6	Hapel AJ	2
Evely RS	1	Hariharan IK	1
Fabre JW	1	Harrison-Smith M	3
Falco J	1	Hartley L	2
Faulkner-Jones B	1	Harvey RP	1
Fitzgerald TJ	1	Haskill S	1
Foote S	2	Hibberd AD	1
Foster R Jr	3	Hilton AA	1
Fowler KJ	1	Hilton DJ	34
Fox R	10	Hoang T-K	4
Fung MC	2	Hodgson G	2
Furth M	1	Hood L	1
Gainsford T	2	Howard M	3
Gall JAM	1	Hunkapillar M	1
Garland J	1	Ihle J	1
Garson OM	2	Inglese M	1
Gearing AJ	2	Janoshwitz H	1
Gearing DP	16	Johnson GR	77
Gerondakis S	3	Johnson RM	3
Gilmore DJ	4	Juttner C	3
Goldschneider I	2	Kandiah DA	1
Gonda TJ	7	Kannourakis G	8

Keech J	1	Matsumoto M	1
Kelso A	12	Mauer AB	1
Kimura S	2	McArthur G	5
Kincade P	1	McCarthy JH	4
King J	7	McFarlane C	2
Kirchmyer R	1	McGrath K	4
Kirsch IR	2	McKenzie IFC	1
Klingler K	3	McKinstry W	2
Klinken P	2	McNeall J	1
Klintworth GJ	2	McNeill T	5
Kolber S	1	McNiece I	1
Köntgen F	5	McPhee D	1
Kozka IJ	1	Merchav S	1
Lala PK	1	Mermod J-J	3
Lang RA	4	Metcalf D	327
Layton JE	10	Mifsud S	4
Layton MJ	7	Miller JFAP	3
Leder A	1	Mitchell GF	2
Levin FC	2	Moore JG	2
Levin J	2	Moore MAS	22
Li CL	8	Moritz RL	2
Li R	5	Morstyn G	12
Lieschke GJ	6	Mulligan RC	1
Lindeman GJ	1	Munro AJ	1
Lingelbach SR	1	Murphy V	1
Lock P	5	Murray LJL	1
Lopez AF	13	Nandurkar HH	4
Lyons I	3	Naparstek E	1
MacDonald HR	3	Ng A	1
Maekawa T	5	Ng KW	1
Maher D	7	Nice EC	10
Mak N-K	1	Nicola NA	132
Mandel TE	6	Nicholas WL	1
Mansfield R	4	Nicholson SE	3
Maritz JS	1	Nossal GJV	2
Martin TJ	1	Novak U	3
Mathews RW	1	O'Connor M	1

Odartchenko N	1	Schmidt A	1
Ostertag W	2	Scolnick E	1
Owczarek CM	7	Scott C	1
Owens T	3	Scott D	1
Parker J	3	Shadduck R	3
Parkin S	1	Sheridan JW	7
Pearse M	1	Sheridan W	9
Pease A	1	Shortman K	4
Pennington DG	2	Simpson RJ	10
Penschow JD	1	Sinickas V	1
Pereira A	1	Smith A	1
Peterson L	1	Smith DK	1
Pierce J	1	Sobiesczczuk P	1
Pincus S	1	Sordat B	1
Presneill J	1	Souza LM	1
Rabellino EM	3	Spangrude GJ	2
Raicevic A	1	Sparrow LG	2
Rakar S	4	Spitzer G	3
Rallings M	1	Sprigg NS	1
Rasko JEJ	12	Staber FG	8
Ravich RBM	1	Stahl J	4
Richardson RT	1	Stanley E	5
Robb L	19	Stanley I	3
Roberts AW	10	Stanley R	21
Roberts B	5	Stanton H	3
Roberts TM	1	Starr R	4
Robinson WA	10	Stenning GM	1
Rodger MB	2	Stevens S	1
Rohrschneider L	4	Stewart CL	1
Ross GD	1	Stocker J	1
Rossner MT	4	Strasser A	8
Rubira MR	1	Sullivan JR	2
Russell S	3	Sumner M	4
Sakakeeny MA	1	Sutherland GR	2
Sanderson CJ	2	Szer J	3
Sewell WA	1	Takagi K	1
Scheerlinck J-P Y	1	Tanigawa T	2

Tarlinton D	2	Werkmeister JA	2
Thatcher DR	2	Whittingham S	2
Thomas R	1	Williams N	10
Tran HTT	1	Williams RL	2
Treutlein HR	1	Williamson DJ	10
Ungar B	1	Willson TA	23
Vadas MA	14	Wilson EMA	1
Vairo G	2	Wilson JW	4
Varigos G	1	Wong CG	2
Viney EM	2	Wycherley K	2
Vincent P	1	Yeo GF	1
Villeval J-L	6	Young AM	1
Visvader J	3	Young IG	1
von Melchner H	9	Yumita S	1
Vremec D	2	Zhan YF	2
Wagner EF	1	Zhang J-G	5
Wagner K	1	Zhang Y	2
Wahren B	1	Zittoun R	1
Waldmann H	4		
Walker F	3		
Wall D	1		
Wang EA	1		
Ward LD	3		
Ward M	1		
Waring LJ	3		
Waring PM	9		
Warner N	6		
Warren DJ	2		
Watt SM	8		

Suggested Further Readings

I have chosen not to disrupt the text by insertion of conventional scientific referencing. For those wishing more detailed information, I suggest the following reviews that, in total, contain more than a thousand references and include those specifically referred to in the text.

Armitage JO. Emerging applications of recombinant human granulocyte-macrophage colony-stimulating factor. *Blood* 1998;92:4491-4508.

Blalock WL, Weinstein-Oppenheimer C, Chang F et al. Signal transduction, cell cycle regulatory, and anti-apoptotic pathways regulated by IL-3 in hematopoietic cells: possible sites for intervention with anti-neoplastic drugs. *Leukemia* 1999;13:1109-1166.

Eder M, Giessler G, Ganser A. IL-3 in the clinic. *Stem Cells* 1997; 15:327-333.

Gasson JC. Molecular physiology of granulocyte-macrophage colony-stimulating factor. *Blood* 1991;77:1131-1145.

Grant SM, Heel RC. Recombinant granulocyte-macrophage colony-stimulating factor (rGM-CSF). *Drugs* 1992;43:516-560.

Guthridge MA, Stomski FC, Thomas D et al. Mechanism of activation of the GM-CSF, IL-3, and IL-5 family of receptors. *Stem Cells* 1998;16:301-313.

Hollingshead LM, Goa RL. Recombinant granulocyte colony-stimulating factor (rG-CSF). A review of its pharmacological properties and prospective role in neutropenic conditions. *Drugs* 1991;42:300-330.

Metcalf D. The Charlotte Friend Memorial Lecture. The role of hematopoietic growth factors in the development and suppression of myeloid leukemias. *Leukemia* 1997;11:1599-1604.

Metcalf D. The SOCS-1 story. *Exp Hematol* 1999;27:1715-1723.

Metcalf D, Nicola NA. *The Hemopoietic Colony-Stimulating Factors. From Biology to Clinical Applications.* 1995 Cambridge University Press.

Sheridan W. Cytokine-only approaches to mobilization of progenitor cells. In: Morstyn G, Sheridan W, eds. *Cell Therapy.* Cambridge University Press, 1996:146-182.

Welte K, Dale D. Pathophysiology and treatment of severe chronic neutropenia. *Ann Hematol* 1996;72:158-165.

Welte K, Gabrilove J, Bronchud MH et al. Filgrastim (r-metHuG-CSF): The first 10 years. *Blood* 1996;88:1907-1929.

Index

Alexander, WS 184–185, 194
Ada, G 29
Agar cultures
    discovery 6–15
    use for bioassays 48–58
Amgen 79, 108, 119–120, 132
AMRAD 182–183
Axelrad, AA 93

Begley, CG 149, 162–163, 184
Bioassays
    dubious joys of 47–55
    personal involvement 55–58
    problems with 47–58
Biogen 117–118
Biotechnology Australia 117
Bradley, TR 6–7, 10–14, 17, 19,
    40–42, 64, 147
Buick, RN 171
Burgess, AW 62–69, 74, 86, 110
Burnet, M 18

Camakaris, J 62

Cantrell, MA 114
Carreras, J (Jose) 143
Cetus 118
Chang, JM 190–191
Chervenick, P 94
Chugai 79, 119–120, 132
Colony stimulating factors (CSF)
    action in vitro cell proliferation
        101
    action in vitro cell survival 101
    differentiation commitment
        101–102
    functional activation 81, 102
    actions in vivo 40, 127–137
    autocrine production 172–177
    bioassays 47–58
    clinical trials 139–151
    cloning of genes 107–122
    G–CSF 71–81
    GM–CSF 59–69
    inactivation of genes 187–196
    in infections 133–135
    leukemia induction 167–177

CSF continued
  leukemia suppression 72–76,
    177–186
  M–CSF (CSF–1) 37–43
  Multi–CSF (IL–3) 83–92
  overproduction 189–191
  patent disputes 113–115, 119
  receptors 102–103, 153–158
  regulation of production
    103–104
Cook, WD 173
Cooperative Research Centres
  (CRC), formation of 160–161
Cory, S 177
Cutler, RL 86, 91

DeLamarter, J 117–118
Dexter, TM 86–87, 89–90
DNAX 108
Dranoff, G 193–194
Dresch, C 73
Drinkwater, CM 194–195
Dührsen, U 147, 174–175
Dunn, AR 110–113, 143, 191,
  193–194

Elefanty, AG 184
Erythroid colonies 93–94
Erythropoietin 6, 31, 64

Fox, R 139
Fung, M–C 110
Futter, A 113

Gasson, JC 96
Gearing, DP 137, 155–157
Genetics Institute 108
Gianni, AM 148
Golde, DW 96, 114, 139
Goldschneider, I 99

Gonda, TJ 173–174
Gough, NM 110–113, 137, 143,
  155–157, 175, 181
Grail, D 110
Groopman, JE 139
Gross, L 14

Hilton, DJ 161, 164, 179–181,
  184–185
Hood, LE 69
Horiuchi, M 75
Hozumi, M 179
Human marrow cultures 25,
  168–172
Hunkapillar, MW 69

Ichikawa, Y 14, 17, 45, 72–75,
  178
Ihle, JN 90, 94
Immunex 108, 119–120
Interleukin–1 (IL-1) 97
Interleukin–2 (IL-2) 98, 109
Interleukin–3 (IL–3) (Multi–CSF)
  83–93
Interleukin–4 (IL–4) 181
Interleukin–5 (IL–5) 87–88
Interleukin–6 (IL–6) 109, 181
Ishimoto, A 72

Johnson, GR 65, 73, 77, 85–86
  188–191
Juttner, CA 148

Kawasaki, ES 113, 118
Kelso, A 113
Kindler, V 131
Kishimoto, T 109, 181

Lang, RA 173–174, 189–190
Lee, F 87

Leukemic cell cultures
    AML 171–173
    CML 168–171
Leukemia Inhibitory Factor (LIF)
    cloning 180
    pleiotropic actions 181–184
    purification of 179–181
    receptor 158–159, 165
Lieschke, GJ 191, 194–195
Lopez, AF 81, 102
Lotem, J 74, 180
Ludwig Institute for Cancer
        Research, formation of 67
Lung conditioned medium
    for G–CSF 71–81
    for GM–CSF 60–69

M1 leukemia 72–73, 179–180,
    181–185
McCulloch, EA 22, 44, 104
McNeill, TA 84
Marrow culture, history of 7–11
Matsumoto, M 76
McCarthy, J 65
Merck 182–183
Miyajima, A 157–158
Moore, MAS 28, 62, 83–84, 86,
    90–91, 96, 118
Morstyn, G 139

Nagata, S 81, 96, 118–119, 158
Nice, EC 110
Nicola, NA 2, 65, 67–68, 76–81,
    86–87, 95, 99, 112–113,
    155–158, 160, 175, 184
Nossal, GJV 18–19

Oddo, L (Luba) 113
Oncostatin–M (OSM) 183–184

Paran, M 25
Park, LS 157–158
Parker, JW 84–85
Peripheral Blood Stem Cells
    147–150
Perkins, A 177
Pike, BL 25, 168
Platzer, E 96, 118
Pluznik, DH 14–15
Potter, M 10
Puck, T 9–10, 13, 104
Purification of CSFs
    general approach 36–37
    G–CSF 71–81, 96
    GM–CSF 59–69, 96
    M–CSF (CSF–1) 37–43
    Multi–CSF (IL–3) 83–92

Quilici, C 113, 130

Rasko, JEJ 161, 174
Receptors
    G–CSF 158
    GM–CSF 155–157
    M–CSF (CSF–1) 154–155
    Multi–CSF (IL–3) 157–158
    signaling from 154–155, 164
    substructure 164–165
Regulators
    redundancy 124–126
    synergy 102, 124–126
Research Corporation Technologies
    113
Revel, M 109
Richman, CM 148
Robb, L 162–163, 194–195
Robinson, WM 19, 21, 25, 28, 30,
    168
Rohrschneider, LR 154, 175
Rothwell, VM 154

Russell, S 65

Sachs, L 14–15
Sandoz, 115, 183
Schering Plough 115
Schrader, JW 89–90
Shadduck, RK 72, 75
Sheridan, JW 42, 59–61, 62
Sheridan, WP 148
Sherr, CJ 154–155
Simpson, RJ 69, 79
Souza, LM 96, 118
Sparrow, LG 69, 110
Spleen conditioned medium 84–91
Stanley, E 193–194
Stanley, ER 24–30, 34, 38, 42–43,
    46, 59, 68, 94, 118
Starr, R 185
Stem cell factor (SCF) 88
Stephenson, JR 93
Stevens, S 48
Suppressor of cytokine signaling
    (SOCS–1) 185

Taniguchi, T 109
Tepperman, AD 93–94
Terminology 43–46

Tomida, M 179
Thymus 6
Till, JE 22

Urine, purification of M–CSF from
    33–42

Vadas, MA 81, 102, 120
Villeval, J–L 175, 191

Walker, F 95
Warner, NL 28, 83–84, 92
WEHI–3B leukemia 74–75, 77–78,
    80, 83–84, 91–92
Welte, KE 96, 118
Wiktor–Jedrzejczak, W 192–193
Wiluszynski, Y 113
Wilks, A 164
Williams, DE 104
Williams, RL 181
Willson, TA 137, 162
Wilson, E 65, 66
Wong, GG 114, 118
Wyss, C 83

Yang, Y–C 120
Yokota, T 110